CREATURES
OF THE
ORDER

First published in Great Britain by Twenty Watt,
an imprint of Weldon Owen,
part of Kings Road Publishing Ltd.
3.08 The Plaza,
535 King's Road,
Chelsea, London,
SW10 0SZ

© 2018 Weldon Owen

Consultant: Jules Howard
Authors: Jules Howard and Fay Evans
Illustrator: Kelsey Oseid
Editorial: Fay Evans
Design: Emma Vince
Publisher: Donna Gregory

ISBN: 978-1-7834-2473-3

A CIP catalogue for this book is available from the British Library

Printed and bound in China

2 4 6 8 10 9 7 5 3 1

20 watt

CREATURES
OF THE
ORDER

ILLUSTRATED BY KELSEY OSEID

20watt

CONTENTS

CREATURES
OF THE
ORDER

INTRODUCTION

Every animal living today is a member of an order, a special type of extended family sharing similar physical traits. Within each order, though there are many different animals, there exists a common theme. Everything is family. This book explores some of Earth's most dazzling taxonomic orders. It celebrates the way that life organizes itself, and the mechanisms through which it does so. It will introduce you to the centuries-old art of taxonomy, which is a scientific way of understanding life. And it aims for you to know more deeply the animals of Earth.

Grey breasted wood wren

Yellow perch

Planet Earth is a swirling, dizzying mass of interacting organisms, but if you look closely beyond its surface, you will see order. Animals are not totally unique. They share features, sometimes with other animals that you thought were totally different! They can be divided into families. They can be classified. There are creatures that give birth, and have backbones and belly buttons, that we call mammals. There are creatures with feathers and wings, that lay shelled eggs, that we call birds. There are creatures that swim and rear tadpoles, and creatures with eight legs that scuttle and crawl, known as amphibians and arachnids respectively. We loosely group animals according to these features, but even within these groups, there is a world of diversity to be ordered.

Consider the mammals. This group includes cats, dogs, wolves, monkeys, and mice, and that's just a start. But these many mammals can be divided up into smaller groups of animals that live in similar ways – that have a common theme. You could say that rats and mice are variations on a nibbling mammal theme. Monkeys and apes are variations within a climbing mammal theme. Wolves and tigers are variations on a theme of pursuit and predation. They are predatory mammals that share the same muscular jaws, big canine teeth, and scissor-like molars, making them masters of the hunt and the kill.

These three groups – nibbling, grasping, killing – exist as families within the larger family of mammals. These are orders of mammal. There are orders of bird, amphibian, and arachnid as well. Orders are a key element within the art of taxonomy – a branch of science that goes back centuries, concerned with classifying biological organisms.

Hawksbill sea turtle

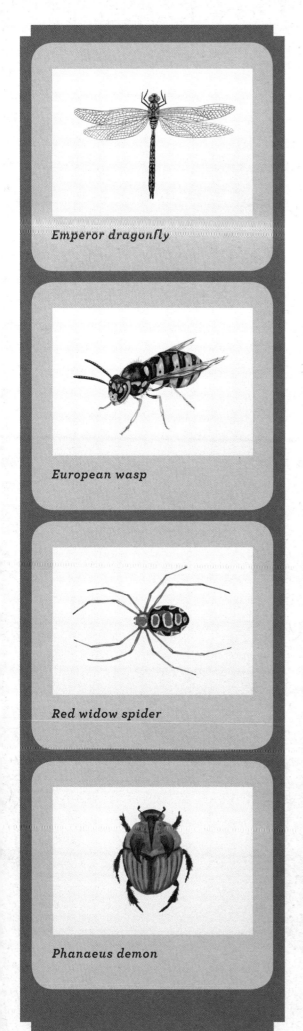

Emperor dragonfly

European wasp

Red widow spider

Phanaeus demon

Taxonomy owes a huge debt to one famous scientist. It was the Swedish naturalist Carl Linnaeus who, in 1735, came upon a clever way of sorting out the complexity of nature by dividing animals up into families, which could then be sub-divided into smaller families, and then even smaller families! He gave these sub-divisions names which are still used today.

Lar gibbon

Every kind of animal (and plant) has a unique species name. Each and every one of these species is part of a genus of closely related creatures, which is part of a larger proper family grouping. Related families make up an order of animals that sit within a larger grouping still – the class – which itself sits within a phylum and then, further, a kingdom (see pages 8–9). Linnaeus created a logic for understanding biological similarities and differences, and he assigned every animal and plant a place to belong. Now organic life can be categorized and classified. In modern times, classification is the breath-taking work of skilled taxonomists, who each year name thousands upon thousands of new species, and place them within their correct families.

The science of taxonomy revolutionized the way that we consider animals and plant species. This unlocked our understanding of animals within these taxonomic orders, and of how they are variations on a theme of common adaptations. Songbirds (order Passeriformes) are variations on a theme of bird. Wasps, bees, and ants (order Hymenoptera) are variations on a theme of insect. Spiders (order Araneae) are variations on a theme of arachnid. Frogs and toads (order Anura) are variations on a theme of amphibian-kind. It is here, within the taxonomic orders of life that we can marvel at nature's diversity and impressive potential for variety.

Turn the pages of this book and you will see incredible expressions of animal colour, animal size, and animal charisma, but look closely and you will see that each creature has something important in common with every other representative of its taxonomic order. Each illustration in this book represents a unique expression of life on Earth, as every species within a taxonomic order is adapted to a slightly different place or a slightly different way of life.

This book is a celebration of incredible animal diversity, revealed through taxonomy to be nothing more than astounding and beautiful variations on a series of simple themes.

These then, are the Creatures of the Order.

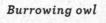

Burrowing owl

ANIMAL CLASSIFICATION

Life on Earth can be divided neatly into categories defined more than two hundred years ago by the Swedish naturalist, Carl Linnaeus. Linnaeus divided thousands of types of animals and plants up into smaller groups, and created a system to organize it. Taxonomy is based on identifying physical details and using them to group similar animals and plants together, and it also uses the fossil records and DNA to find common ancestors. When a new species is discovered, scientists look at its features very carefully, to decide where it belongs within the great family tree of life.

DOMAIN

The three domains that make up all life on Earth are archaea, bacteria, and eukarya. All multi-celled organisms (animals, plants, and fungi) are eukarya. Creatures are divided between these groups based on the types of DNA within their cells.

KINGDOM

By looking even closer at the types of cells that organisms are made up of, the creatures of Earth can be split into recognizable kingdoms. These include the animal, plant, and fungi kingdoms.

PHYLUM

All of the members of a phylum contain the same basic features which often relate to their body plan. Arthropoda, for instance, is a phylum that incorporates all joint-legged creatures with external skeletons.

CLASS

Phyla can be sub-divided into manageable chunks (classes) which are based on broad body characteristics. Of vertebrates (animals with a central backbone), the classes include mammals, amphibians, reptiles, and birds.

ORDER

Classes can be separated into groups of orders. Orders are made up of animals with similar noteworthy features. Rodents, for instance, are an order of mammals with elongated front teeth (incisors) that carry on growing through life.

FAMILY

Many orders have within them families of animals adapted to different ways of life. Tarantulas, for instance, are a family of hairy spiders called Theraphosidae, which specialize in feeding on large invertebrates.

GENUS

This sub-division of a family makes crucial divisions between closely-related groups of animals. For instance, though horses and donkeys are different animals, they are both creatures of the same genus (Equus).

SPECIES

The classic definition of a species is a group of organisms that can interbreed and produce offspring which can themselves go on to have babies. There may be more than 8 million different species on Earth.

BINOMIAL NAMING

By classifying organisms in this way, every creature on Earth has its own scientific name, shortened (most commonly) down to genus and species name – their so-called "binomial" name. In most books (including this one) you will see the scientific name written in italics after the species' common name. For instance, the animal pictured below will be described as a grey wolf *Canis lupus*.

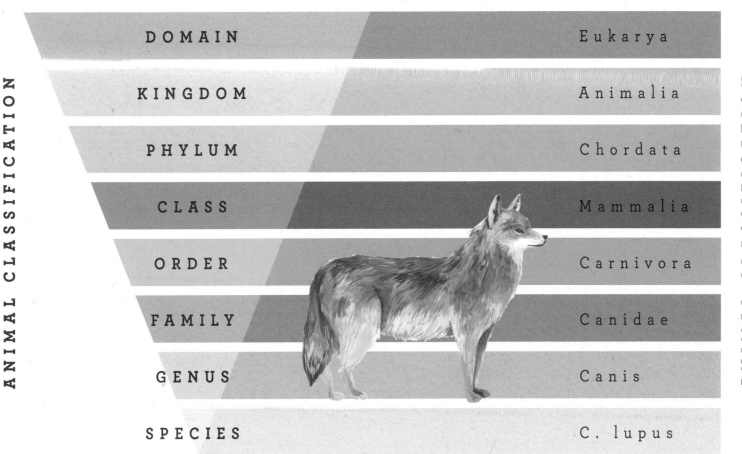

ANIMAL CLASSIFICATION

ANIMAL CLASSIFICATION of the Grey Wolf

DOMAIN	Eukarya
KINGDOM	Animalia
PHYLUM	Chordata
CLASS	Mammalia
ORDER	Carnivora
FAMILY	Canidae
GENUS	Canis
SPECIES	C. lupus

ANIMAL CLASSIFICATION
of the Isabella Tiger Moth

DOMAIN	Eukarya
KINGDOM	Animalia
PHYLUM	Arthropoda
CLASS	Insecta
ORDER	Lepidoptera
FAMILY	Erebidae
GENUS	Pyrrharctia
SPECIES	P. isabella

ANIMAL CLASSIFICATION
of the Bottlenose Dolphin

DOMAIN	Eukarya
KINGDOM	Animalia
PHYLUM	Chordata
CLASS	Mammalia
ORDER	Cetacea
FAMILY	Delphinidae
GENUS	Tursiops
SPECIES	T. truncatus

EVOLUTION OF ORDERS

Through the pages of this book, you will see that the creatures of every order share features – legs, wings, stingers, teeth – that they have inherited from creatures that lived before them. Fossils, DNA, and the shared characteristics of animals living today tell us that life evolved from shared ancestors. In other words, every order listed in this book is made up of family members – they are distant cousins and they share the same ancient grandparents.

CENOZOIC
66 million years ago

Within a few million years of the meteorite that destroyed most of the dinosaurs, mammal survivors split into a number of recognizable orders, many of which survive and rule in the modern age. Of the bird survivors, two noteworthy orders have come to dominate the skies – the owls (Strigiformes) and the perching songbirds (Passeriformes).

1. *Strigiformes*
2. *Primates*
3. *Carnivora*
4. *Cetacea*
5. *Rodentia*
6. *Passeriformes*

MESOZOIC
252–66 million years ago

The Mesozoic era is sometimes called the Age of Reptiles, and can be broken down into three time periods, starting from the most recent.

Cretaceous As the clock ticked toward their sad demise, only a single part of the sprawling dinosaur family survived – the birds. Of the Cretaceous bird orders, the Galliformes still survive to this day.

Jurassic The dinosaurs co-existed alongside a host of newly sprouting orders including the frogs and toads (Anura), snakes and lizards (Squamata), dragonflies and damselflies (Odonata), and butterflies and moths (Lepidoptera).

Triassic As the Earth recovered from a mass extinction event that rocked the world before dinosaurs, the stage was set for a number of advancing reptiles including a newly evolving order of turtles, tortoises, and terrapins (Testudines).

7. *Galliformes*
8. *Perciformes*
9. *Squamata*
10. *Odonata*
11. *Lepidoptera*
12. *Anura*
13. *Hymenoptera*
14. *Testudines*

PALAEOZOIC
541–252 million years ago

The Palaeozoic era was the period before the dinosaurs became established. What had been an empty landscape was being colonized by amphibians and early reptiles. Among the reptiles were creatures that would later come to be called lizards, turtles, dinosaurs, and mammals. The first invertebrates (animals without backbones) were numerous during this stage. In fact, early invertebrate orders that evolved in this age live today. They include the spiders and beetles.

15. *Orthoptera*
16. *Araneae*
17. *Coleoptera*
18. *Decapoda*
19. *Isopods*
20. *Scorpiones*
21. *Hemiptera*

WHERE DO ORDERS COME FROM?

A timeline of orders

Orders sprout when creatures hit upon an adaptation that offers new potential to flourish and can be passed on to future generations. Whales and dolphins, for instance, evolved from a single species of hoofed mammal that lived 50 million years and took to water. Likewise, every beetle alive today has evolved from a simple insect that developed hard wings that later became the shelled casing that gives beetles their unique protection. In this way, the animals of every order on Earth are variations on a theme of successful adaptation. Their ancestors succeeded long ago and continued to evolve over time in their own special ways, toward the present day.

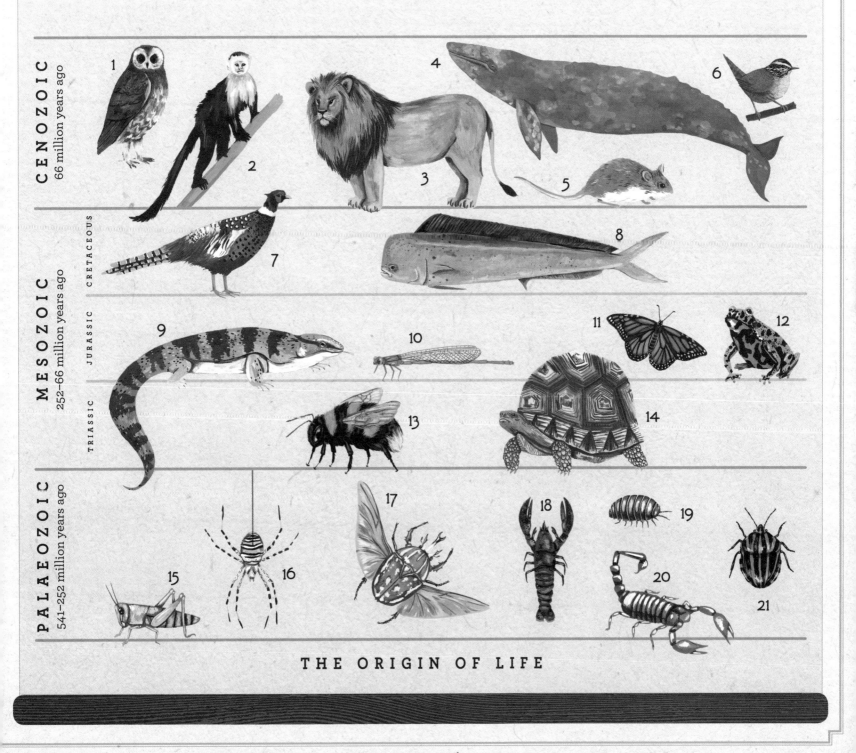

CENOZOIC 66 million years ago

MESOZOIC 252–66 million years ago

CRETACEOUS · JURASSIC · TRIASSIC

PALAEOZOIC 541–252 million years ago

THE ORIGIN OF LIFE

CREATURES

OF THE

ORDER

CARNIVORA

FROM LATIN CARN "FLESH" + VORĀRE "TO DEVOUR"

Carnivora is an order of mammals characterized as hunters and scavengers. In total, there are 280 "carnivorans", each possessing strong jaw muscles, sharp teeth, and forward-facing eyes, along with typical mammalian traits such as giving birth to live babies and warm-bloodedness. In their relative sizes, the Carnivora are one of the most diverse of any mammalian order. They range from the palm-sized least weasel *Mustela nivalis*, to the polar bear *Ursus maritimus*, which can weigh up to 1,000 kg (2,200 lbs), and the southern elephant seal *Mirounga leonina*, which can reach 5,000 kg (11,000 lbs) and measure up to 7 m (20 ft) in length.

1. HONEY BADGER

The honey badger is not actually a badger – it's more like a ferret. It's known as the world's most fearless creature, and has teeth that can break through the shell of a tortoise.

2. STELLAR SEA LION

Stellars are the biggest of all sea lions, and they have an appetite to match. They are also part of a smaller family, the pinnipeds – carnivorous, aquatic mammals.

3. RED PANDA

Don't be fooled by the name of the order – the red panda does not eat meat. Red pandas also have an extra, sixth "finger" – an extension of their wrist bone that helps them hold onto bamboo and to climb

4. RED FOX

Red foxes live all around the world in lots of different habitats. They are known to be intelligent and cunning – probably because of their resourcefulness.

Red fox

5. BROWN BEAR

A female brown bear will hibernate all winter long, and may not even wake up to give birth. The cubs feed and sleep until she wakes up – and they're much bigger by then!

6. RIVER OTTER

North American river otters can stay underwater for up to eight minutes at a time. When they do this, they shut both of their nostrils and ears tightly, so no water gets in.

7. BLACK BEAR

Black bears move quite slowly when walking, but can run at speeds of up to 40–50 km/h (25–30 mph). Despite the name, they can also be light brown, blue-grey, or even blonde.

8. WHITE-TAILED MONGOOSE

The white-tailed mongoose is the largest of the mongoose species. Mongooses are omnivores, and eat insects, berries, mice, and even snakes.

9. RACCOON

The front paws of a raccoon are similar to a human's hand. They have five fingers, which help them catch fish and even (some say) unlock doors!

Grey wolf

10. GREY WOLF

Grey wolves are social animals that live in packs of up to 30 other wolves. They communicate with the pack by howling, barking, scent marking, and even dancing.

11. CHEETAH

The cheetah is the fastest land animal on Earth and can reach speeds of 113 km/h (70 mph). They use their tails like boat rudders to help them steer at high speeds.

12. MANED WOLF

Despite its name, this beautiful, fox-coloured carnivore is not actually a wolf. It has a large mane on the back of its neck that becomes raised if the animal senses danger.

Maned wolf

Meerkat

Canada lynx

Fennec fox

13. MEERKAT

Meerkats have an amazing sense of smell. They communicate with each other vocally – they have special noises that warn the colony about different threats. The meerkat belongs to the mongoose family.

14. LION

The lion has the loudest roar of any big cat – it can be heard up to 8 km (5 miles) away. Unlike other big cats, lions live together in large "prides". The female lions hunt and raise their cubs together.

15. WALRUS

Walrus tusks never stop growing, and the animals use them to pull themselves out of the water. They spend half of their lives in the sea, and can dive to depths of 80 m (260 ft).

16. STRIPED SKUNK

Skunks are most famous for their powerful defence mechanism – their horrible, hard-to-remove stink! Skunk spray is an oily liquid produced by glands under the animals' tails.

17. BLACK-BACKED JACKAL

Jackals are one of the few species of mammal that mate for life. Because of this, you'll often find them living in pairs.

18. SABLE

Sables sometimes follow the tracks of wolves or bears to eat what is left of their meals. They also eat slugs.

19. AFRICAN CIVET

The African civet is a nocturnal animal that is closely related to weasels and mongooses. Each African civet has a unique pattern of spots and streaks on its body.

20. CANADA LYNX

The Canada lynx mainly hunts the snowshoe hare. They are so dependent on them that the lynx population drops whenever the hare population does.

21. LEAST WEASEL

The least weasel is the smallest weasel. Weasels in the northern, coldest parts of their range turn completely white in the winter, and when put under an Ultraviolet light, they glow a bright lavender colour.

22. LEOPARD

Leopards are incredibly agile and strong – they can jump up to 6 m (20 ft) horizontally, and up to 3 m (10 ft) vertically. They also have amazing hearing, and can hear up to five times as well as humans do.

23. TIGER

Tigers are one of the only big cats who love water. They are excellent swimmers, and use the water to hunt and to cool off.

24. HARP SEAL

A harp seal can identify her baby from among hundreds of other baby seals using her sense of smell. Pups are completely white when they are born, and become grey with black spots after about two weeks.

25. SPOTTED HYENA

Spotted hyenas have a powerful digestive system. They can eat the bones, skin, and teeth from their prey and have even been found to eat objects made from aluminium.

Spotted hyena

26. FENNEC FOX

Fennec foxes have very furry paws, which help them walk across hot sand in the desert. As well as protecting the foxes against the heat, they also keep their toes toasty during the night when temperatures drop below zero.

27. ELEPHANT SEAL

Elephant seals have a clever trick that allows them to go for long periods of time without drinking. Their kidneys make concentrated urine that has more waste and less water in it.

28. FANALOKA

The fanaloka can only be found on the island of Madagascar. Their diet consists of insects, bird eggs, and small reptiles – but in the winter they live off the fat that is stored in their tails.

29. KINKAJOU

The kinkajou uses its tail like an additional arm. The thick, strong tail can be used to climb trees, keep balance, and during cold nights, even as a blanket to keep warm.

30. AMERICAN MINK

Like skunks, American minks can spray a horrible-smelling liquid to scare off predators. However, they can't aim their spray like a skunk can.

FIGURE 1. MAMMAL FAMILIES
Panthera leo family

As with almost all mammals, members of the order Carnivora give birth to live young, and nurse their offspring with milk. Though the gestation period (the length of the pregnancy) can vary, all Carnivora conceive, carry the offspring to term in the adult female's uterus, and give birth.

In most species of the order Carnivora, the mother has exclusive (or at the very least primary) care of the offspring. From the time of their birth, they will remain with their mother as she protects them, feeds them (first with milk, then with prey), and teaches them how to live. Many offspring will stay with their mother for a number of years.

FIGURE 2. CHARACTER
Carnivore jaw

Members of the order Carnivora have a particularly characteristic skull shape. They have relatively large brains, heavy skulls, and jaws that are made for crushing food with force. The masseter, a muscle in the jaw that aids chewing, is found only in mammals. In the order Carnivora, this muscle is attached to the lower jaw, which can only move up and down, not side to side.

These animals also have well-developed, very prominent canine teeth, strong incisors, and their cheek teeth (molars) usually have sharp edges. These features aid them in the shearing and tearing of their prey (usually, but not always, meat).

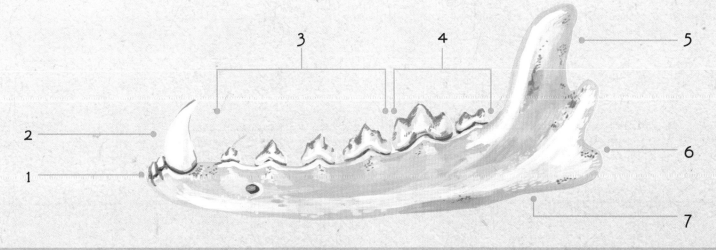

1. Incisors
2. Canine
3. Premolars
4. Molars
5. Coronoid process
6. Mandibular condyle
7. Angular process

CETACEA

FROM LATIN CETUS "WHALE" + GREEK KETOS "HUGE FISH"

Cetaceans are some of the biggest creatures to ever have lived. Some, like the blue whale *Balaenoptera musculus*, can reach 30 m (98 ft) in length and weigh more than 36 elephants. Though adapted to life underwater, Cetaceans retain a host of familiar mammalian features. Like all mammals, they are air-breathers and give birth to live young that they nourish with milk. All Cetaceans are brilliant communicators and some, like dolphins, use this talent to help them hunt (through echolocation). Once considered to be their own distinct order, Cetaceans have more recently been redefined as a particularly charismatic side-branch of a larger mammalian order, Artiodactyla.

1. BELUGA WHALE
Bright white beluga whales are easy to spot and are very social animals. It's not uncommon to spot them in pods numbering in the hundreds!

2. DWARF SPINNER DOLPHIN
Spinner dolphins are well known for jumping, flipping, and spinning out above the water. They are very social animals, often seeking out humans.

3. MELON-HEADED WHALE
Melon-headed whales are able to swim very quickly – especially if startled! They often like to spend the day resting at the surface of the water.

4. KILLER WHALE
Killer whales, or orcas, actually belong to the dolphin family. They are incredibly intelligent, and often work together in groups to catch prey.

Killer whale

Atlantic spotted dolphin

5. ATLANTIC SPOTTED DOLPHIN
These dolphins are born completely grey, and develop their spots as they grow. They usually live in smaller pods, and eat mostly small fish, squid, and octopus.

6. HOURGLASS DOLPHIN
The hourglass dolphin is sometimes called the "sea cow" because of its black and white colouring. These animals are rarely seen near shore.

7. DWARF SPERM WHALE
This whale is considered to be the smallest in the whale family. It can grow to around 2.7 m (9 ft) long – little more than the size of a dolphin.

8. NARWHAL
The narwhal is called the "unicorn of the sea", because of a long, tusk-like tooth that protrudes from the front of its head. Narwhals can grow up to 5.5 m (18 ft) long.

9. DUSKY DOLPHIN
Dusky dolphins love leaping out of the water, and they are often seen approaching boats so that they can bow ride (surfing in the waves created by boats and ships).

10. FALSE KILLER WHALE
This whale is a large dolphin that looks like a killer whale, but isn't. This secretive animal was once thought to be extinct, but dwindling populations remain in the open ocean.

11. HARBOUR PORPOISE
The harbour porpoise is one of six kinds of porpoise. As its name would make you think, it likes to stay close to the coast, harbours, and is even found in rivers and estuaries.

12. HUMPBACK WHALE
The humpback whale grows to an average length of 18 m (60 ft), and eats 1,360 kg (1.5 tons) of food a day! It eats tiny fish and krill, which are small, shrimp-like animals.

13. BOTTLENOSE DOLPHIN
Perhaps the most well known dolphin, these clever mammals can communicate with one another using clicks and songs, and can even teach each other survival tricks in the wild.

14. RISSO'S DOLPHIN

The Risso's dolphin lives in warm tropical waters around the world. These dolphins are covered in lots of scars, made by their prey, squid, and social interactions with other dolphins.

15. SPERM WHALE

The sperm whale is the largest toothed whale and can grow to become over 18 m (60 ft) long. It also has the largest brain of any animal on Earth.

16. SHEPHERD'S BEAKED WHALE

The Sheperd's beaked whale can reach lengths of 7 m (24 ft). Unusually for whales, males have a pair of enlarged teeth (or tusks) on their lower jaws, possibly used for display or fighting.

17. VAQUITA

The vaquita is the rarest marine animal in the world. It's an extremely endangered creature – it is thought that there may be as few as thirty of these porpoises left in the world.

18. LA PLATA DOLPHIN

The La Plata dolphin has the longest beak (in relation to body size) of any of the Cetaceans. It is a river dolphin that lives in saltwater esturies and oceans.

19. PYGMY RIGHT WHALE

Until 2012, the pygmy right whale was thought to be extinct. It is the smallest of the baleen whales and is closely related to an extinct family of whales, making it a living fossil.

20. CLYMENE DOLPHIN

Sometimes mistaken for the spinner dolphin, the clymene dolphin is an active swimmer and is often seen approaching boats, riding the boat waves and jumping out of the water.

21. LONG-FINNED PILOT WHALE

These whales are, like killer whales, part of the dolphin family. They have been observed to "babysit" calves that are not their own within their family groups.

22. GRAY'S BEAKED WHALE

Apart from the Shepherd's beaked whale, this is the only beaked whale that has upper teeth. It also has a long and particularly thin beak.

23. PINK RIVER DOLPHIN

The pink river dolphin (also known as the boto) is the largest species of river dolphin. Newborns have dark grey skin, and by the time they are adults their skin has turned pink.

24. FINLESS PORPOISE

Found in and around the Yangtzee river, the finless porpoise is the only porpoise to lack a true dorsal fin. Instead, it has a low ridge in its back, covered in tiny growths.

25. HECTOR'S BEAKED WHALE

These beaked whales lack functional teeth, so probably capture their prey using suction.

26. GREY WHALE

These whales can grow up to 15 m (50 ft) long and have the longest migration of any mammal. They travel a 16,000–19,000 km (10,000 – 12,000 mile) round trip every year between the western coast of Mexico and the Arctic seas.

Hector's dolphin

27. SEI WHALE

The sei whale can reach lengths of 20 m (65 ft), and is one of the fastest whales, reaching speeds of up to 48 km/h (30 mph).

28. HECTOR'S DOLPHIN

Hector's dolphins are one of the smallest and rarest types of the dolphins. They live in either all male or all female groups of 2–8 dolphins.

29. CUVIER'S BEAKED WHALE

In 2011, a tagged Cuvier's beaked whale dived to 2,992 m (9,800 ft) – the deepest dive recorded by any mammal. These whales can fold down their rib cages to stop air pockets forming in their lungs, and to decrease their buoyancy.

30. DWARF MINKE WHALE

When attacked, minke whales may not regularly defend themselves, choosing instead to flee at high speed. They can maintain speeds of 24–48 km/h (15–30 mph) for up to an hour.

Grey whale

FIGURE 1. GREY WHALE SKELETON
Eschrichtius robustus

The first cetaceans evolved more than 50 million years ago from a land-living carnivorous mammal. Over a period of 10 million years, fossils show that feet that were once used for scurrying over rocks became more adept at swimming, lengthening for efficiency. The links to land living cousins are still evident within the order Cetacea. They still have the bones of fingers within their flippers (see annotations 3–6), though most (but not all) have lost the signs of their hind legs altogether over time.

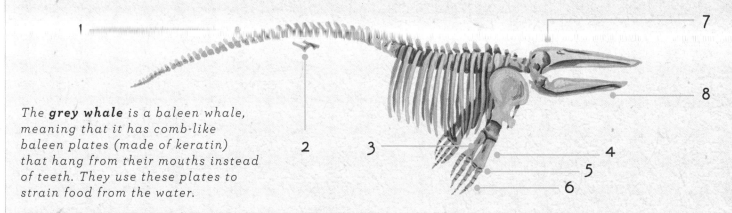

*The **grey whale** is a baleen whale, meaning that it has comb-like baleen plates (made of keratin) that hang from their mouths instead of teeth. They use these plates to strain food from the water.*

1. *Caudal vertebrae*
2. *Pelvis*
3. *Radius*
4. *Ulna*
5. *Carpals and metacarpals*
6. *Phalanges*
7. *Skull*
8. *Mandible*

FIGURE 2. ECHOLOCATION
Biosonar in toothed whales

Many toothed whales, including dolphins and porpoises, communicate and hunt using echolocation. Though they have good eyesight both above and below the water, echolocation (also called biosonar) helps them locate and identify different things underwater, like prey or other objects and creatures. By using echolocation, they are able to determine the size, shape, and the speed the object is travelling.

To make the click noises needed for echolocation, they produce sounds with their larynx and a complicated system of cavities in the head that are connected to the blow holes. The sounds that they make are a quick series of clicks that cover a wide range of high frequencies.

All toothed whales have an organ at the front of their heads called a "melon". This fat-filled organ focuses and directs the sound waves that they emit from their head. Another fat-filled cavity in their lower-jaw receives this sound, and the information is sent to the middle ear before being read by the brain. The time elapsed between the first click and how long it takes to receive the sound wave (the echo) back is what tells them how far away an object is.

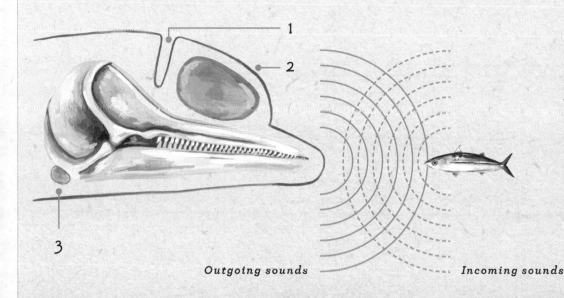

1. *Blowhole*
2. *Melon*
3. *Auditory bullae*

*The sound bounces off the object and echoes back to the **dolphin**. From this they can detect the object's size, shape, distance, and speed.*

Outgoing sounds   *Incoming sounds*

PRIMATES

Primates are known for their big brains, communicative chatter, and well-developed forward-facing eyes. Largely adapted to life in the trees, Primates have long fingers and grasping hands, and most (except apes) possess a long tail that assists balance. Some species, like the brown howler monkey *Alouatta guariba*, can use their tails to grasp branches. Primates exhibit great diversity in size, from the enormous eastern gorilla *Gorilla beringei* to Madame Berthe's mouse lemur *Microcebus berthae* which could sit quite comfortably on the end of a human thumb. More than half of all Primate species are threatened with extinction, making this one of the fastest declining animal orders on Earth.

1. PHILIPPINE TARSIER
The Philippine tarsier is one of the smallest primates, reaching only 7.6–16 cm (3–6.3 in) in height, and is around the size of an adult human's fist.

2. LAR GIBBON
Lar gibbons can vary in colour, from black or dark brown, to a light-brown or sandy colour. Fifty percent of the lar gibbon's diet is fruit, with the rest being leaves, insects, and flowers.

3. EMPEROR TAMARIN
Emperor tamarins have very distinctive long, white moustaches which grow down to below their shoulders.

4. POTTO
As part of their courting rituals, pottos will often hang upside down and groom each other. The potto has a very distinct smell that some people have said smells like curry.

5. BROWN HOWLER MONKEY
Found only in the Atlantic Forest in South America, the brown howler monkey is known for its howls and roars. It has special vocal chords to make these very specific sounds.

6. RED-SHANKED DOUC
The red-shanked douc is one of the most colourful primates. It has red "socks" from its knees to its ankles, white forearms, black hands and feet, and pale blue eyelids.

7. MADAME BERTHE'S MOUSE LEMUR
This mouse lemur is the smallest primate in the world, reaching only 11 cm (4.3 in) in length, with a tail up to 14 cm (5.5 in) long. Like all other lemurs, they are only found on the island of Madagascar.

8. RING-TAILED LEMUR
Ring-tailed lemurs are extremely social and live in female-dominated groups of up to 30 lemurs. They use specific vocal calls to alert the rest of the group to any danger.

Ring-tailed lemur

9. WHITE-FACED SAKI
If a predator is near, white-faced sakis will call out an alarm which can last well over an hour. They will then all puff up their fur, and stamp their feet against the trees or the ground to intimidate any possible predators.

10. RED RUFFED LEMUR
As the name suggests, this lemur has reddish, rust-coloured fur with a black face, hands and feet, and tail. It spends a lot of time grooming, and has lower teeth that grow in a slighty spaced line, creating a special "toothcomb".

11. GOLDEN LION TAMARIN
The golden lion tamarin is not related to lions at all, but is named for its glorious mane. It has distinctive, bright orange fur and a dark, hairless face.

12. WHITE-HEADED CAPUCHIN
These monkeys are highly intelligent, and have learned to use tools to get to food, as well as for weapons. They have also been observed rubbing plants all over their bodies, possibly as a type of herbal medicine.

Aye-aye

Grey-backed sportive lemur

13. AYE-AYE
Originally classified as a rodent because of its looks, the aye-aye is actually a lemur. It has a very long, thin, middle finger which it uses to tap on branches to check for insects and then to scoop them out.

14. GOLDEN SNUB-NOSED MONKEY
The golden snub-nosed monkey lives in groups of 5–10 within bands of up to 600! When there is danger, the young are placed at the centre of the group and the strongest males investigate the cause of alarm.

15. FRANÇOIS' LANGUR
This primate is unique because it has a very complex stomach, made up of multiple chambers. This is because it has a folivorous diet – it eats only leaves, and needs to break down the complex cellulose.

16. GREY-BELLIED NIGHT MONKEY
The nocturnal night monkey sleeps in holes in trees by day, and travels through the canopy of trees in the South American sub-tropical forests looking for fruit, insects, and nectar.

17. INDRI
The indri is one of the largest lemurs in existence, and is well known for its loud and very distinctive calls. It calls to communicate things like territories and warning of danger.

18. JAPANESE MACAQUE
Also known as snow monkeys, these monkeys are famous for soaking in hot springs to keep warm during the cold winter months.

19. BORNEAN ORANGUTAN
Bornean orangutans are critically endangered due to habitat destruction and hunting. They are only found on the island of Borneo.

20. PRINCE BERNHARD'S TITI
Prince Bernhard's titis mate for life, and live together in groups of pairs. The bond between the male titi and the infant is very strong, with the male carrying the infant on his back and only bringing it to its mother to be fed.

21. BALD UAKARI
Bald uakari have an extremely striking, bright crimson face, a bald head, and a long, fair coat. They only have short tails, but can move through the trees without any problems.

22. BEMARAHA WOOLLY LEMUR
These nocturnal lemurs sleep through the day and come out at night to feed and groom each other. They stay in contact by using loud, distinctive whistles.

23. PYGMY MARMOSET
The pygmy marmoset's diet is very different to that of most Primates. Pygmy marmosets use their sharp teeth to drain sap and gum from trees.

24. SUNDA SLOW LORIS
The slow loris is generally quite a solitary animal, preferring to spend its time alone. However, it forms monogamous mating pairs who stay together until the offspring is ready to survive on their own

25. CENTRAL AMERICAN SQUIRREL MONKEY
Like many other primates, this squirrel monkey is arboreal, which means it moves through the trees. Because of its diet, it plays an important role in dispersing seeds and polinating flowers.

26. GREY-BACKED SPORTIVE LEMUR
The grey-backed sportive lemur is one of the smallest members of the lemur family. It is currently a vulnerable species due to habitat destruction.

27. PROBOSCIS MONKEY
The proboscis monkey is one of the largest species of monkey in Asia. It is famous for the male's large nose, which can be so long that it hangs lower than his mouth.

28. SENEGAL BUSHBABY
These African creatures have amazing ears, like radar dishes! Their ears are made up of four separate parts which they can bend individually to help them hear insects while they're hunting.

29. MANDRILL
Mandrill are very recognizable, with the male's exotic colouring. They have bright red and blue noses and rumps, and yellow beards.

30. WESTERN GORILLA
Gorillas are the largest of the great apes, though eastern gorillas are larger than western ones. Mature male gorillas are called silverbacks, and can weigh up to 158 kg (350 lbs). Female gorillas are smaller, and can weigh up to 81 kg (180 lbs).

FIGURE 1.
MANDRILL SKELETON
Mandrillus sphinx

Primates evolved from tree-living mammals around 10–15 million years after the dinosaurs died out and their tree-living, history is written into their bones.

They have five strong, dextrous fingers which assist them with climbing, and many species in the order also possess a flexible tail, useful for gripping branches.

Primates differ from most other mammals because they have a skull that sits at the top of their spine rather than in front of it. This feature, along with a strong pelvis, allows them to move and sit upright.

Primates also have large brains (relative to other mammals), and stereoscopic vision.

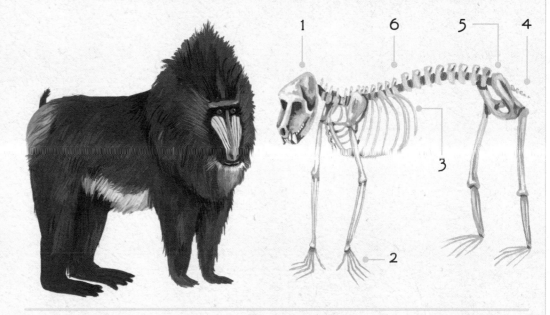

1. *Skull*
2. *Fingers and thumb*
3. *Ribs*
4. *Tail*
5. *Pelvis*
6. *Spine*

FIGURE 2. ORANG-UTAN SKULL
Pongo pygmaeus

Primates are different to most other mammals in that they possess forward-facing eyes. This adaption allows for improved vision, with eyes positioned to take in the most stimuli and allow for greater depth perception. This can be extremely helpful, especially for Primates living in arboreal environments (like forests).

Unlike most mammals, many Primates have colour vision. This adaptation helps them to spot berries and other coloured fruits in the canopy.

Orangutan

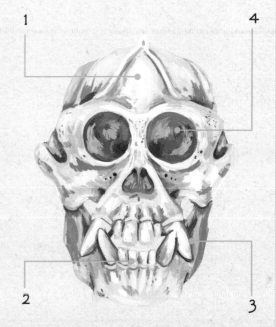

Primate skulls allow for larger brains, and subsequently their brains are relatively larger than those of other mammals. While many theories exist regarding the reason for their larger brains, it is thought that their social behaviour, their occasional ability to use tools, and their ability to solve problems are all part of this.

Primates have generalized teeth – incisors, canines, and molars. These teeth are adapted to eating a wide variety of foods. The incisors are used for biting off bits of food, the canines are for piercing and tearing, and the molars are used for grinding the food. Humans possess the same charismatic teeth patterns as other apes.

1. *Cranium*
2. *Incisors*
3. *Canines*
4. *Forward-facing eye sockets*

RODENTIA

FROM LATIN RODERE "TO GNAW"

Of all the mammalian orders, the rodents are one of the most effective at adapting to new habitats. Representatives of this order flourish in polar regions, dry deserts, and even in the most urban cities on Earth where, often, they thrive in their millions. Like most mammals, rodents possess molar teeth (called cheek teeth), but unlike most mammals, their front teeth (incisors) grow constantly throughout their lives rather than being replaced. Their ability to gnaw gives rodents an edge over other mammals when it comes to finding and exploiting new food sources. The brown rat *Rattus norvegicus* and the house mouse *Mus musculus* may be the most numerous mammals on Earth, outnumbering even humans.

1. THIRTEEN-LINED GROUND SQUIRREL

During hibernation, this squirrel will roll up in a tight ball and decrease its breaths from 200 breaths per minute to just one breath every five minutes. It is also known as the striped gopher.

2. LOWLAND PACA

These large rodents are found in tropical parts of South America. They live near water, and are excellent swimmers, sometimes fleeing into water to escape danger. They are also excellent climbers, and will climb trees to search for food.

3. MOUSE-LIKE HAMSTER

Though they were originally thought to be part of the hamster family due to the shape of their teeth, they do not have the cheek pouches or short tails that all hamsters have.

4. NORTH AMERICAN BEAVER

This beaver is the largest rodent in North America, and one of the largest in the world. Beavers are semi-aquatic, and have a special membrane that covers their eyes so that they can see underwater. Their ears and nostrils can be sealed too.

5. MALABAR SPINY DORMOUSE

This distinctively bushy-tailed dormouse is only found in India, where it lives an arboreal life, living inside holes in the trees. It eats fruits, and is considered to be a pest around pepper plantations.

6. EURASIAN RED SQUIRREL

Once found all over Britain and Ireland, the omnivorous red squirrel's numbers have decreased drastically in recent years due to the introduction of the North American grey squirrel, as well as habitat loss. They are still common throughout Eurasia.

7. FOUR-TOED JERBOA

Four-toed jerboas are small rodents that get around by hopping. They have long, clawed hind feet and short forelegs. Their long tails help to support them when they stand upright.

Four-toed jerboa

8. DEGU

Degus are extremely social. They work together to build large and elaborate burrows underground, and coordinate their digging activity, even forming digging chains. Sometimes the females who have nested communally will even feed each others' young.

9. BLACK-TAILED PRAIRIE DOG

Prairie dogs live in large communities, called towns or villages. There can be thousands of individuals in one of these communities, all separated into smaller families, called coteries.

10. GARDEN DORMOUSE

These nocturnal dormice can be found in southern Europe. They sleep in sphere-shaped nests in trees during the day, then at night they forage and hunt for food.

11. PACARANA

The pacarana is a large and slow-moving rodent that typically lives in families of four or five. It is found only in the tropical rainforests in the Amazon River Basin and in the foothills of the Andes.

12. DASSIE RAT

The dassie rat is the only remaining member of the family Petromuridae, a name that literally translates as, "rock mouse". They are extremely good at fitting into very confined spaces, and have a specially adapted skull and ribs to allow this.

13. LAOTIAN ROCK RAT

Loatian rock rats look like rats, but with big bushy tails, similar to those of squirrels. They are slow moving, and slightly duck-footed, but are able to quickly scale the rocky terrain of their habitat.

14. MALAGASY GIANT RAT

The malagasy giant rat is only found on the island of Madagascar. They live in monogamous pairs, and the males are known for being incredibly protective of their young, even putting themselves in danger to follow or defend the young.

15. COMMON AGOUTI

The common agouti feeds on fruit, nuts, leaves, and roots. Agoutis sit on their hind legs and hold their food between their front paws to feed. They can sometimes be seen feeding in groups of up to 100 animals.

16. NORWAY LEMMING

During the winter, Norway lemmings live in insulated shelters below the snow. These spaces give them warmth, protection from predators, and access to food. They can either dig their own spaces, or live in ones that have already been formed underground.

17. SOUTH AFRICAN SPRINGHARE

The South African springhare looks like a small kangaroo, with well-developed legs that allow it to leap over 2 m (6 ft 7 in) in a single bound. They grow up to 47 cm (19 in) in length (including the tail).

South African springhare

18. DEER MOUSE

There are many species of deer mouse, but *Peromyscus maniculatus* is among the most adaptable. Their nests have been found in the ground, in logs, in abandoned vehicles, and even 24 m (80 ft) above the ground in a Douglas fir tree.

19. NORTHERN FLYING SQUIRREL

These flying squirrels can be clumsy while walking on the ground, but they are excellent gliders. They have great manoeuvrability while in the air, making 90 degree turns around obstacles if they have to.

20. POCKET GOPHER

Pocket gophers have large cheek pouches, which they use to store food as they travel around their extensive tunnel systems to get back to their home burrows.

21. COYPU

The coypu, or river rat, lives near water, and eats plants and roots – it will eat up to 25 percent of its body weight every day. Originally only found in South America, it has since been introduced in North America, Asia, Europe, and Africa.

22. SHORT-TAILED CHINCHILLA

The short-tailed chinchilla is an endangered rodent from South America. Chinchillas tend to live in groups, and are well adapted to cold climates because of their dense fur.

23. COMMON GUNDI

The common gundi lives in rocky habitats in northern Africa, finding shelter in the rock crevices. It does not drink, as it gets enough water to survive from its food.

24. PATAGONIAN MARA

Patagonian maras may look like rabbits, or small deer, but they are rodents. They are found only in Argentina, where they prefer habitats with plenty of shrubs for cover.

Fresno kangaroo rat

25. FRESNO KANGAROO RAT

The smallest of the kangaroo rats, it reaches only 10 cm (4 in) long, though its tail is longer than the rest of its body! It uses its long tail to balance as it leaps about.

26. PREVOST'S SQUIRREL

The Prevost's squirrel is one of the most colourful rodents, with black, reddish-orange, and white fur. It is also sometimes called the Asian tri-coloured squirrel.

27. CAPYBARA

The capybara is the largest rodent in the world and has been recorded to grow to weigh 91 kg (200 lbs). When a female is ready to mate, she will whistle through her nose to let males know.

28. NAKED MOLE RAT

This mole rat has an incredible ability to survive without oxygen for a long period of time. It can live for up to 18 minutes completely without oxygen by altering its metabolism to power its cells with fructose instead. This process is usually only seen in plants.

29. TUCO-TUCO

The tuco-tuco gets its name from the "tuc-tuc" noise it makes as it digs its burrows. These animals spend 90 percent of their lives underground in their burrows.

30. CRESTED PORCUPINE

This easily recognizable rodent's body is covered in long, coarse quills that run along the head, neck, and back. Porcupines are able to raise these into a crest, as a threat or defence mechanism.

FIGURE 1. SENSORY SYSTEM
Peromyscus maniculatus

The Rodentia have a heightened sensory system. They have evolved this way because they are at high risk of predation from many other animals.

Many species in the order Rodentia have large ears that they can move independently, and have excellent hearing (mice and rats in particular can hear at extremely high frequencies).

All rodents have whiskers. Whiskers are hairs that grow out of a hair follicle that is sealed by a blood sinus. When a whisker is touched, it pushes against the blood, and a nerve ending is stimulated which then sends a message to the brain. They use their whiskers to help them when they are unable to rely on sight to find food and to move safely in their environment.

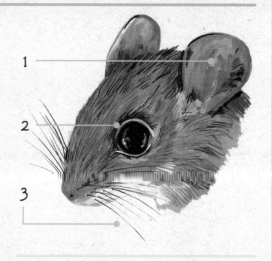

1. *Large ears*
2. *Eyes*
3. *Whiskers*

Deer mouse

FIGURE 2. RODENTIA
Continually growing incisors

Creatures in the order Rodentia are equipped with a pair of razor sharp, continuously growing incisors. The order Rodentia's arrangement of teeth can be traced back to the Palaeocene era where they first evolved in Asia.

Most rodents can have up to 22 teeth, (often four incisors and twelve molars) and a large gap (a diastema) between them. The two incisors work together like a pair of scissors, slicing the food to make it possible to chew with their molars. Rodents use the gap between the teeth by filling it with their cheeks while they are gnawing. This way, any non-edible items that get into their mouths fall out before they reach their molars.

Rodents must gnaw and file their teeth down to stop them from becoming overgrown, and to keep them sharp.

The muscles in a rodent's jaw also help them to use their specialist teeth. The jaw moves not only in an up and down movement, but in a forward and backward movement to help with the gnawing. This also helps during the filing of the incisors – their jaws pull forward to stop the molars from wearing away.

If a creature in the order Rodentia breaks its incisors, it will likely die because it will not be able to eat.

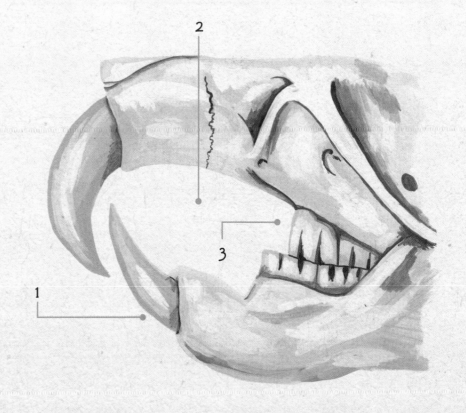

1. *Incisors*
2. *Diastema*
3. *Molars*

PASSERIFORMES

FROM LATIN PASSER "SPARROWS" + FORME "FORMS"

With more than 5,000 species, the order Passeriformes includes half of all bird species on Earth. The secret behind their success comes mainly from a simple adaptation – a toe arrangement that allows for perching on tree branches, rocks, and cliffs. Passerine chicks are often defenceless and blind when first hatched, requiring lots of parental investment from both males and females. This requires them to be notably territorial birds. Often, they are colourful. Males of many species depend on rich and vibrant feather patterns to convey their health to prospective mates. Some, like the birds-of-paradise, have elaborate trailing feathers and dancing displays that we celebrate as one of nature's finest spectacles.

1. WHITE-NECKED ROCKFOWL
White-necked rockfowl are monogamous birds, and produce two eggs, twice a year. They build their nests out of mud, usually in caves.

2. BLACK-CAPPED CHICKADEE
On cold nights, these small birds can reduce their body temperature from 42°C (107°F) to around 30°C (86°F) to conserve energy. They usually live in flocks in the winter, but can be territorial in the breeding season.

3. CANADA WARBLER
The Canada warbler spends winter in South America and migrates to North America to breed. It spends less than two months there, being one of the last to arrive, and one of the first to leave.

4. BARN SWALLOW
Barn swallows feed during flight, snatching insects out of the air. They fly using quick turns and dives, and can catch their prey between just above the ground to 30 m (100 ft) up in the air.

5. STELLER'S JAY
This unmistakable dark blue bird has a dark brown or black crest with white or blue markings. Along with the blue jay, the Steller's jay is one of the only jays that uses mud to build its nests.

6. BALTIMORE ORIOLE
The female Baltimore oriole builds its nest using plant or animal materials that have been tightly woven together. These nests hang from the undersides of branches.

7. PAINTED BUNTING
The male painted bunting has brightly coloured feathers, with a blue head, red breast, and green wings. The female is slightly duller, but still bright green.

8. BLACK-CHINNED BABBLER
The black-chinned babbler has a yellow-brown body, and very distinctive black markings around its eyes and on its chin.

9. GREY-BREASTED WOOD WREN
These small, brown, black, and grey birds are widely distributed. They can be found from Mexico all the way down through South America to Bolivia.

Grey-breasted wood wren

Olive-backed sunbird

10. OLIVE-BACKED SUNBIRD
Both the male and female olive-backed sunbirds have yellow bodies, but the males also have a bright blue face. They feed on nectar, which they can reach by hovering or perching.

11. AUSTRALIAN LOGRUNNER
Australian logrunners feed on insects, which they find by foraging on the forest floor. They scratch through the leaf debris with their feet, leaving cleared circles in the forest floor behind them.

12. HOUSE SPARROW
Native to Europe, the Mediterranean, and Asia, the house sparrow has also been introduced to Australia, Africa, and the Americas – this makes it probably the most widely distributed wild bird on Earth.

13. RAGGIANA BIRD-OF-PARADISE

Found in New Guinea, the males are easily recognizable by their lacy, reddish-pink feathers which can grow up to 60 cm (20 in) long!

14. AUSTRALIAN GOLDEN WHISTLER

These birds build their nests out of twigs, grass, and bark, held together with spiderwebs. The male and the female build the nest together.

15. GOLDEN-CROWNED KINGLET

This bird's song is very high pitched – so high pitched, in fact, that the golden-crowned kinglet's song is one of the first bird songs that people stop being able to hear as they get older.

16. CHESTNUT-TAILED STARLING

The two sub-species of chestnut-tailed starling can be told apart by the colour of their underparts. The plumage of the *blythii* is a dull orange, and the *nemoricola* is a dull orange and white.

17. SPOTTED PARDALOTE

This tiny bird only grows up to 10 cm (4 in) in length, and weighs around 6 g (0.21 oz), making it one of the smallest birds found in Australia.

18. FAIRY BLUEBIRD

Fairy bluebirds eat mostly fruit and possibly some insects. They forage in groups on the forest floor, and will crush fruit that is too big to make it more manageable.

19. WOODLARK

These ground-nesting birds prefer to live in areas with short vegetation, and forestry plantations – the fallen trees provide good cover for them to nest and a good supply of food.

20. WHITE-BREASTED NUTHATCH

Like other nuthatches, the white-breasted nuthatch makes its home in the hole of a tree. It sometimes even smears insects around the hole to deter squirrels!

Opal-crowned manakin

21. OPAL-CROWNED MANAKIN

The opal-crowned manakin has a green body and a white, iridescent patch of feathers on the top of its head. It is found around the Amazon in Brazil.

22. BRIDLED TITMOUSE

Outside of breeding season, the bridled titmouse can be seen flocking together with other species of birds like chickadees, warblers, nuthatches, and creepers.

23. YELLOW-THROATED VIREO

The yellow-throated vireo builds its nest in the fork of a small branch in a tree. The nest, made of bark, dry grasses, pine needles, and leaves, is held together with spiderwebs and hangs down in between the branches.

24. WHITE-EYED SLATY FLYCATCHER

This lively African bird breeds in the north before migrating south to avoid the cold. They eat insects, catching them on the wing.

25. BOHEMIAN WAXWING

The Bohemian waxwing's favourite food is the rowan berry. These birds can metabolize alcohol found in fermenting fruit, but still sometimes become intoxicated!

Bohemian waxwing

European robin

26. EUROPEAN ROBIN

This instantly recognizable bird has an orange breast, brown body, and white belly. While the males are incredibly territorial, and can be aggressive, they are relatively unafraid of people, and often forage for food in gardens.

27. HERMIT THRUSH

The hermit thrush can be found across North America, depending on the season. East of the Rocky Mountains, they will usually nest on the ground, while west of them, they will usually nest in trees.

28. NORTHERN CARDINAL

These songbirds are extremely territorial, marking out their territory with song. They mate for life, and the male will usually bring the female nest material which she will then build with.

29. AMERICAN CROW

The American crow is one of only a few birds that has been seen using tools to get to its food. Crows understand water displacement, and have been seen using sticks to dig food out of deep holes.

30. BROWN DIPPER

The brown dipper hunts by wading into shallow streams and picking small organisms out of the bottom. The adults can also dive in slightly deeper streams, to get larger organisms.

31. VOGELKOP BOWERBIRD

The Vogelkop bowerbird is named for the bower structure that it makes: a cone-shaped, hut-like structure with an entrance and a cleared out "lawn" area at the front which they decorate with berries, flowers, stones, leaves, or even beetle shells.

FIGURE 1. PASSERINE FOOT SHAPE
Anisodactyl allignment

Passeriformes evolved around 55 million years ago, and spread across the world to become one of the most diverse of all the bird groups. Each of the 5,000 individual species of Passeriformes possess a foot-shape that allows for perching, with three toes pointing forward, and one toe pointing backward. This toe alignment is known as *anisodactyl* and allows the bird to perch on vertical surfaces, like trees or cliffs.

They have few nerves or blood vessels in their feet, which allows them to land on cold perches and wires in freezing weather.

To stay in place while they fall asleep while perching, special flexor tendons in their legs tighten, meaning that their toes lock around the perch automatically. They will stay this way until they straighten their legs.

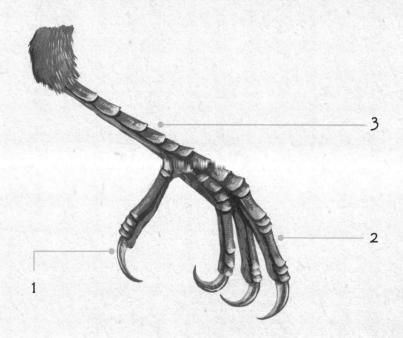

Passeriformes, like most other birds, walk up on their toes instead of on their entire foot.

1. *One toe pointing backwards*
2. *Three front-pointing toes*
3. *Tarsometatarsus bone*

FIGURE 2. SONGBIRDS
Oscines

Most Passeriformes are vocal in fact, nearly all Passeriformes sing, which gives them their nickname – the songbirds. Their vocal organ has developed in a particular way that has allowed them to produce complicated songs.

Passeriformes use songs for many things. Their songs are territorial, they signal the location of individual birds to others, and they also signal their availability to mate. The preference of the female birds for a male bird is heavily influenced by the songs that he sings. For many species, the more songs in a male bird's repertoire, the more females he might attract.

There are only a few species outside the songbirds that have well-developed songs, and the songs that they sing are not to be confused with bird calls that signal alarm or contact, which all species of bird use.

Golden-crowned kinglet, Australian golden whistler, White-eyed slaty flycatcher, Hermit thrush, Black-capped chickadee.

STRIGIFORMES

FROM THE LATIN STRIG (STRIX) "OWL", + FORME "SHAPE, LOOK"

Of the 200 or so owl species that survive today, most are solitary hunters that specialize in aerial attacks on their unsuspecting prey. All possess large eyes for prey-spotting, and serrated wing feathers that muffle the sound of their approach. Owls are among the most cosmopolitan of all bird orders, occupying every continent on Earth except Antarctica. Most Strigiformes are nocturnal predators that primarily eat rodents, but some species, like the Serendib scops owl *Otus thilohoffmanni*, are known to consume beetles and earthworms. Though primarily creatures of the trees, some Strigiformes have adapted to grasslands and prairies, most notably the burrowing owl *Athene cunicularia*.

1. BARN OWL

The barn owl can fly almost silently – this allows it to hear even the slightest sound made by its prey on the forest floor below. It eats voles, rats, mice, and other small rodents.

2. NORTHERN PYGMY OWL

The northern pygmy owl can raise a pair of tufts on the sides of its head when threatened by a predator to make itself look more threatening.

3. POWERFUL OWL

Powerful owls live together permanently in pairs. It is said, that during the breeding season, the female powerful owl will lay her eggs on almost exactly the same day every year.

4. GREAT HORNED OWL

Great horned owls are carnivores that will eat almost anything smaller than them that moves – hares, mice, ducks, squirrels, bats, weasels, and more. They also sometimes eat carrion.

5. CRESTED OWL

Like many owls, the crested owl is a "cavity nester" – they live in tree holes, tree stumps, caves, and sometimes even the lofts in people's houses!

6. SERENDIB SCOPS OWL

The scops owl mostly hunts insects like beetles and moths. They hunt at night, during the first two hours of darkness, and stay close to the ground.

7. ELF OWL

This tiny owl is not aggressive, and prefers to fly away rather than fight. If caught, it will sometimes play dead until danger has passed.

8. GREATER SOOTY OWL

The greater sooty owl has a very distinctive voice. It is a downscale shriek, which has been called a "bomb whistle". This is because it is said to sound like a falling bomb, but without the final explosion!

9. ORIENTAL BAY OWL

The oriental bay owl will usually roost no more than 2 m (6.5 ft) above the forest floor. This is because it hunts from a perch, flying through the dense tree branches to make a kill.

10. LONG-WHISKERED OWLET

The long-whiskered owlet usually grows to around 15 cm (6 in) tall, and has long facial whiskers around its beak and eyes.

Spotted wood owl

11. SPOTTED WOOD OWL

The adult spotted wood owl is around 48 cm (18 in) tall, with a wingspan of around 60 cm (27 in). Some make nests by resting loose twigs and leaves on top of branches.

12. GREAT GREY OWL

The great grey owl is the world's largest species of owl by height (but not by weight). These owls have excellent hearing, and can locate and capture prey moving beneath 60 cm (2 ft) of snow using their hearing alone.

13. FOREST OWLET

This endangered owl is found only in the forests of India. The forest owlet eats lizards, rodents, insects, and frogs. It sometimes stores food caches in the hollows of trees.

Cuban screech owl

14. CUBAN SCREECH OWL

Also known as the bare-legged owl, the Cuban screech owl has long, bare legs, unlike most other owls whose legs are covered in feathers.

15. SPECTACLED OWL

The spectacled owl is named as such because it looks like it is wearing glasses. These owls have brown bodies, a light coloured chest, and a dark brown face with white eyebrows and bright yellow-orange eyes.

16. TAWNY OWL

Tawny owls have especially soft, fine fringe on their feathers so that they can swoop down silently onto their prey. Their wings are shorter to make manoeuvring through the trees easier.

17. COLLARED SCOPS OWL

These nocturnal owls are very small, growing to a maximum of 25 cm (10 in) long, and they weigh no more than 170 g (6 oz) – that's less than half a can of soup.

18. BARRED OWL

The barred owl hides in dense foliage during the day. The biggest threat to barred owls is the great horned owl, and they will often move out of their territory if one is near.

19. FLAMMULATED OWL

This owl only grows up to 15cm (6 in) long and is named for the flame shaped markings on its face.

20. STRIPED OWL

Striped owls usually nest on the ground in low shrubs and grasses. In some cases they return to the same area to nest a few years in a row.

21. EASTERN SCREECH OWL

The eastern screech owl has a green-grey beak, while the western screech owl has a grey-black one, making it possible to tell these similar owls apart.

22. CLOUD-FOREST PYGMY OWL

This pygmy owl has two dark spots on the back of its head. These "false eye-spots" fool bigger birds and some predators into thinking that they are aware of their presence.

23. FEARFUL OWL

The fearful owl is the top predator in its territory, but the species is currently threatened by large-scale logging and deforestation.

24. MARSH OWL

These owls have darkly ringed eyes and very small ear tufts. The male marsh owl claims territory by flying over the area he wishes to claim, clapping his wings together and croaking.

25. NORTHERN SAW-WHET OWL

The northern saw-whet owl has extremely sophisticated hearing. This allows it to very precisely localize its prey – so much so that it can hunt in complete darkness by hearing alone.

26. BURROWING OWL

These owls roost and make their nests in burrows in the ground (like those made by prairie dogs). They also have long legs that allow them to sprint as well as to fly while hunting.

Burrowing owl

Spot-bellied eagle owl

27. SPOT-BELLIED EAGLE OWL

This owl is well known in Sri Lanka for its strange, almost human-sounding call. It even matches the description of the legendary "Devil Bird", whose call is thought to be an omen for death.

28. SNOWY OWL

This large, easily recognizable owl can grow up to 70 cm (28 in) long with a wingspan of 150 cm (59 in). The male is completely white and the female is white with black spots.

29. NORTHERN WHITE-FACED OWL

This owl has an amazing talent for disguise. When faced with a predator, it flares its wings out to look much bigger, and when faced with a creature much larger than itself, it contorts itself to best blend in with its surroundings.

30. NORTHERN HAWK-OWL

These hawk-owls are active during the day and hunt mainly lemmings and voles. During breeding season, the male will show off different nesting sites, and the female will choose one.

31. SHORT-EARED OWL

The short-eared owl can be found on every continent except Antarctica and Australia. They are recognizable by the little tufts of feathers on their heads that resemble mammal-type ears.

FIGURE 1. GREAT HORNED OWL SKULL
Bubo virginianus

Owls have evolved to have forward-facing eyes, a hawk-like beak, and conspicuous circles of feathers around each eye. Like many other creatures, they possess eyes that allow for binocular vision, but they cannot move their eyes in their sockets.

Owl eyes are so large that they make up 1–5 percent of the owl's entire body weight. They are held in place by the sclerotic rings in the skull – this is the reason that an owl cannot move its eyes. To compensate, owls have developed the ability to turn their heads almost all the way around.

Though owls have incredible long-distance vision, their close-up vision is much more limited. They have to use their whiskers to help them do anything requiring close contact (like feeding chicks).

Great horned owl

1. *Sclerotic Ring*
2. *Zygomatic Arch*
3. *Nasal Aperture*
4. *Beak*
5. *Lower Mandible*
6. *Infraorbital Canal*

FIGURE 2. SNOWY OWL, ROTATING HEAD
Bubo scandiacus

Members of the order Strigiformes are able to rotate their heads on their necks as much as 270 degrees around, which compensates for how little they are able to move their eyes. An owl's body is specially adapted to enable this to happen. While humans have seven neck vertebrae, owls have fourteen, allowing for much more movement. They also have special adaptations in their circulatory systems which allows them to rotate their heads without cutting off the blood supply to the brain. The tissue and blood vessels are able to flex, so they aren't damaged when the owls turn their heads.

Owls have just one occipital articulation (a bone at the back of the skull – humans have two of these bones). This bone is situated at the top of the backbone, and allows an owl to move its neck in a pivoting movement.

*As the **snowy owl** rotates its head, it is able to see up to 270 degrees around itself.*

GALLIFORMES

FROM LATIN GALLUS "COCK, ROOSTER", + FORME "FORMS"

With muscular legs, sharp claws, and the ability to produce a cacophony of noisy shrieks and bellows, the Galliformes are charismatic birds that specialize in roaming the floors of forests and grasslands. Many plants depend on them to spread seeds, which they do through their droppings. Galliformes are particularly famous for the showy behaviour of males, whose head flaps and beak combs are a sign of reproductive quality to nearby females. Some species, like the green peafowl *Pavo muticus*, are among the most decorated of all birds. They have short wings, suitible for brief flight, and tend to walk or run rather than fly.

1. GREEN JUNGLEFOWL

The male green junglefowl has a brightly coloured plume with a black and almost iridescent body. The female is mostly brown with some green feathers.

2. HORNED CURASSOW

This extremely endangered bird is named for the long, blue horn protruding from its head. The mysterious purpose for this crest has long been argued about.

3. OCELLATED TURKEY

This bird looks more like a peacock than the kind of turkey that you're probably used to seeing. They are vibrantly coloured and don't have the same "beard" that most turkeys have.

4. CRESTED PARTRIDGE

Both the male and female crested partridge share the red ring around the eye, though they are completely different colours. The male is black with iridescent feathers, and the female is olive-green with black wings.

Kalij pheasant

5. KALIJ PHEASANT

Kalij pheasants are native to southern Asia, but have also been introduced to Big Island in Hawaii. They live in tropical and subtropical forests.

6. AUSTRALIAN BRUSH TURKEY

This turkey incubates its eggs in a large mound in the ground. The male will keep the eggs at a constant temperature of 33–38°C (91–100°F) by sticking his beak into the ground to check, and then adding or taking away dirt and leaves.

7. VULTURINE GUINEAFOWL

With its bald head, this African guineafowl looks a lot like a vulture. However, it feeds on seeds, insects, and small spiders – not carrion.

8. CHUKAR PARTRIDGE

Before they can fly properly, chukar partridge chicks practise running up steep inclines with their wings extended. This behaviour could be part of how birds evolved to fly.

9. GOLDEN PHEASANT

Though they are native to China, brightly coloured golden pheasants can now be found in the UK and Ireland, USA, South America, France, and Germany.

10. GREY PARTRIDGE

These orange-faced partridges eat mostly seeds, but they will lead their chicks to forage for and eat insects for the first ten days of their life as a supply of protein.

11. ORANGE-FOOTED SCRUBFOWL

The female has to work very hard to take in enough food to make an egg that is more than 20 percent of her body mass. She does this every 9–20 days.

Crested partridge

Orange-footed scrubfowl

12. RING-NECKED PHEASANT

Male ring-necked pheasants have a distinctive white collar around their necks. They are native to Asia, but have been introduced around the world as a game bird.

13. INDIAN PEAFOWL

This bird is well known for the male of the species, the peacock, who displays a bright blue body and incredibly famous tail feathers, which are covered in bright eyespots.

14. PLAIN CHACHALACA

This bird prefers to escape danger by running away, or leaping and gliding through the bushes and foliage.

15. GREATER PRAIRIE CHICKEN

The greater prairie chicken almost went extinct during the 1930s due to hunting by humans and habitat loss. They are now classed as vulnerable.

16. HELMETED GUINEAFOWL

Named for their featherless, helmet-like head, these large birds rarely fly, but often walk up to 10 km (6 miles) a day while foraging.

17. WILLOW PTARMIGAN

During the winter, the North American species of willow ptarmigan turn completely white. This helps them to be camouflaged when they roost in the snow at night.

18. GREAT CURASSOW

The male great curassow has a distinctive curly crest on its head, and there are three different kinds of female – barred, brown, and black.

19. MALEO

Maleos dig deep holes to lay their eggs in. They bury each egg securely and leave, never returning. The chick will hatch fully formed. It will dig its way out of the hole and be able to fly and feed itself immediately.

Yellow-necked spurfowl

20. YELLOW-NECKED SPURFOWL

This African bird has a yellow patch on its neck and a red eye patch. They forage for insects in dirt and dung.

21. SATYR TRAGOPAN

Also known as the crimson horned pheasant, the male tragopan has a black body and a bright red head. Males also grow blue horns and a wattle during mating season.

22. PALAWAN PEACOCK-PHEASANT

Like many other birds, the male and female look very different. The female is mostly brown with a white face. The male has black and iridescent electric-blue feathers and green-blue eye-spots.

23. SPRUCE GROUSE

The spruce grouse relies on camouflage to stay safe from predators, and has a remarkable ability to stay completely immobile, letting predators come within touching distance before taking flight.

24. HIMALAYAN MONAL

The Himalayan monal is under threat from poaching because of their fantastically-coloured, metallic-like feathers. It is seen as a status symbol in some countries to wear the crest.

25. MOUNTAIN QUAIL

Mountain quails use different techniques to get food. They forage in the ground, use their feet to dig for bulbs, and jump up from the ground to reach berries and seeds on plants.

Siamese fireback

26. SIAMESE FIREBACK

The male Siamese fireback is well known for the long crest of feathers on its head. The crest sticks straight up when the bird becomes excited.

27. SICKLE-WINGED GUAN

This quiet bird has a distinctive blue face. Guans live in small groups in South America, and forage for seeds and nuts.

28. RED JUNGLEFOWL

Thought to be the ancestor of the domesticated chicken, the red junglefowl was first domesticated at least five thousand years ago in Asia.

29. WILD TURKEY

Wild turkeys make a lot of different calls and noises, and their famous "gobble" noise can carry for up to 25 m (83 ft).

30. CALIFORNIA QUAIL

Both sexes of California quail have a forward-dropping head plume that is shaped like a comma. They live in large groups and forage for food.

31. GREEN PEAFOWL

The green peafowl is the closest relative of the Indian peafowl. Unlike other peafowl, male and the female green peafowl are similar in appearance, though the female lacks the magnificent tail.

FIGURE 1. DOMESTICATION AND GALLIFORME FAMILIES
Junglefowl Family

Galliformes are survivors of an ancient branch of the bird family tree. Many are large bodied, sometimes clumsy in flight, and they have muscular, scaly legs. They have made fields and forest floors their own, and are often preyed upon by humans.

Some species of Galliformes have a long-standing relationship with humans, having been domesticated over thousands of years. They are found in nearly every region on Earth, and the first domesticated Galliforme, the chicken, was domesticated in Southern Asia over 5,000 years ago.

Families of chickens, turkeys, and some other species have been kept by humans for years, using their eggs and raising the chicks for food.

*Adult male **junglefowl**.*

Eggs

Chicks

Adult female

FIGURE 2. SEXUAL DIMORPHISM AND MATING
Pavo cristatus

Sexual dimorphism is when males and females of a species differ in certain ways from one another, including in size and colour. In many orders, sexual dimorphism can be very common among species. In the Galliformes, the differences between males and females is at its most spectacular.

Male Galliformes are well known for using a mixture of techniques to attract females for mating. Many make a lot of noise, using loud screams and gobbles, some perform a special dance, and some, like the Indian peafowl *Pavo cristatus*, possess bright headgear and colourful tail feathers that can be rattled to draw the attention of a passing female.

The peafowl has one of the most dramatic examples of sexual dimorphism, with the female having barely any of the showy male's colouring.

*A female and male **Indian peafowl**.*

CREATURES OF THE ORDER | PERCIFORMES

PERCIFORMES

FROM LATIN PERCA (PERCI) "PERCH", + FORME "SHAPED, LOOK"

Of all the orders of vertebrates (animals with backbones) Perciformes are the most plentiful, consisting of more than 10,000 species. They range from the tiny stout infantfish *Schindleria brevipinguis*, barely the size of a grain of rice, to the Atlantic blue marlin *Makaira nigricans* at more than 4 m (13 ft). Perciformes (or "perch-like fish") are united in possessing distinctive arrangements of fins supported by moveable spines. Representatives exist in every aquatic habitat on Earth including the polar regions and the deep sea. There are even Perciformes, like the mudskipper *Periophthalmus barbarus*, that can climb out of the water and live in trees.

1. SHORTBILL SPEARFISH
Native to the Pacific and Indian oceans, the shortbill spearfish can grow to be more than 2 m (7 ft) long and weigh up to 52 kg (115 lbs). It is thought that they only live up to 5 years.

2. ISLAND MACKEREL
The island mackerel are a species of "true" mackerel, and can grow up to 20 cm (8 in) long. They live in large schools and feed on plankton.

3. GREAT BARRACUDA
Great barracudas are large fish with powerful jaws. They have strong, fang-like teeth that jut outwards, and they catch their prey by lying in wait and ambushing them at high speeds.

4. YELLOW PERCH
This freshwater fish has a yellow body with olive-coloured stripes. They live together in schools, preferring to live among weeds and other vegetation.

5. INDIAN GLASSY FISH
Also known as the x-ray fish, the Indian Glassy fish has a transparent body, allowing you to see the bones and internal organs.

Indian glassy fish

Humpback red snapper

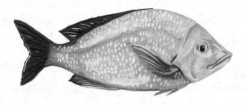

6. HUMPBACK RED SNAPPER
The humpback red snapper lives in coral reefs and can grow up to 50 cm (19 in) long. It has yellow colouring around its eyes, gills, and mouth.

7. DEEPBODY BOARFISH
This reddish-pink fish is usually found at depths of up to 300 m (984 ft), close to the bottom of the ocean where they can find their prey of small crustaceans.

8. OCELLARIS CLOWNFISH
This clownfish has different patterns depending on where they are from. They are black, orange, and red-brown with white stripes.

9. CARAMEL DRUMMER
These fish are known for dispersing their eggs as they swim, leaving them floating freely in the water.

10. MOORISH IDOL
Sometimes mistaken for butterfly fish because they both have a striped body and a long, trailing dorsal fin, the moorish idol has a black, triangular tail fin.

11. CORAL HAWKFISH
This hawkfish has a white body with reddish pink spots, and is usually found in tropical coral reefs in the Pacific ocean. It is sometimes called the pixy or spotted hawkfish.

12. BANDED ARCHERFISH
The archerfish eat crustaceans, small fish, and insects, and are known for their hunting tactics. They can shoot a stream of water up to 1.5 m (5 ft) away to knock an insect off a leaf or a branch, then rush in to grab it between their teeth.

13. DWARF GOURAMI
This incredibly colourful fish is a labyrinth fish – it has a special labyrinth organ that allows it to breathe air from the surface of the water. This can be helpful when the fish is in water with low oxygen content.

14. MOONFISH
Also known as *Mene maculata*, is the only member of its genus that is still living today. All other members of the genus Mene, and the family Menidae, are extinct.

White-barred wrasse

Speckled sandperch

15. WHITE-BARRED WRASSE

Unlike other types of wrasse, this colourful fish has pale, vertical white lines along its body instead of the more often seen horizontal ones.

16. BLOCH'S BIGEYE

These nocturnal fish are sometimes able to change their colour from all red to red with silver blotches. Their large eyes help them take in more light.

17. SOHAL SURGEONFISH

These surgeonfish are named for the razor-sharp, blade-like fins near their tail which they can raise up and use to slash at other fish when disturbed.

18. FIRE DARTFISH

Fire dartfish live in burrows on the upper parts of outer reef slopes. During breeding, once the eggs have been laid, the male carries the eggs in his mouth until they hatch. During this time the male cannot feed at all.

19. ATLANTIC MUDSKIPPER

The Atlantic mudskipper famously can leave the water and cross over mud flats, using its pectoral fins to propel itself. It manages to breathe while crossing the mud by trapping water in its large gill chambers and using this as a supply of oxygen.

20. COMMON DOLPHINFISH

The common dolphinfish, or mahi-mahi, is a large fish found in temperate seas. Mahi-mahi means "very strong" in Hawaiian.

21. LARGE-BANDED BLENNY

These fish are incredibly territorial, and they will aggressively defend their homes from other fish, crustaceans, or invertebrates that come too close.

22. THREADFIN BUTTERFLYFISH

Though most threadfin butterflyfish have dark, false-eye spots on their tails, the ones that you find in the Red Sea do not have this spot.

23. SPOTTED WEEVER

These bottom-dwelling fish are highly venomous, and have specially adapted spines along their backs to deliver venom to anyone or anything that gets too close.

24. FRESHWATER ANGELFISH

Despite their beauty, these angelfish are fierce ambush predators. They lay their eggs on submerged logs and fallen leaves, and are highly adept at hiding among roots and plants.

25. LOOKDOWN

The lookdown has a large, flat-fronted head and was one of the creatures first described by Carl Linnaeus, the "father of taxonomy", in 1758.

26. FRENCH ANGELFISH

Many French angelfish mate for life, and monogomous pairs will fiercely defend their territory against other neighbouring pairs.

27. BLUEGILL

The bluegill is a North American fish that has been introduced into lakes all over the world. Bluegills live in shallow waters in lakes and ponds, and hide inside fallen logs or clusters of weeds.

28. SPECKLED SANDPERCH

Also known as grubfish, these fish live in the sand under solid pieces of reef. Like many Perciformes, some members of the sandperch family are able to change sex, starting their adult lives as females and changing their sex to male later in life.

29. COMMON REMORA

The common remora has a dorsal fin that acts like a suction cup, allowing it to attach itself to larger animals. The host provides the remora with fast-moving water to bathe its gills, while providing food, transport, and protection.

30. LARGE KELPFISH

As larval young, kelpfish sometimes school together with transparent mysid shrimp. Young kelpfish can change their skin colours very quickly, particularly the females who can change in mere moments.

31. SOUTHERN SHEEPSHEAD

The front teeth of the southern sheepshead fish closely resemble human teeth. Unlike humans, they have many rows of these short, stubby teeth.

Bluegill

FIGURE 1.
PERCIFORME SKELETON
Perca flavescens (yellow perch)

The order of Perciformes is one of the largest and most diverse orders of creatures on Earth.

Although the creatures of this order can vary hugely in size, they each share some specific features: a bony backbone, two eyes, dorsal fins, anal fins, and pectoral fins.

Nearly all creatures in the order of Perciformes possess a combination of spiny and soft fin rays. Often, the larger frontmost dorsal fin is notably more spiny than the posterior fins (the secondary dorsal and anal fins) which can either be partially or completely separated.

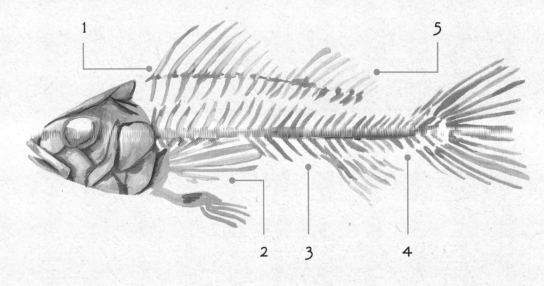

1. *Dermal rays (spiny)*
2. *Pectoral fin*
3. *Ribs*
4. *Hemal spines*
5. *Dermal rays (soft)*

FIGURE 2. SMALLEST TO LARGEST
Paedocypris progenetica
& *Thunnus thynnus* (bluefin tuna)

There are over the 10,000 species found in the order of Perciformes, and they are the largest group of modern bony fishes. They are incredibly diverse, with a huge difference that can be found in size and colour, brought together by a small set of shared characteristics.

Perciformes are the most variably sized order of vertebrates with an enormous difference between the largest and the smallest members of the order. The Atlantic bluefin tuna *Thunnus thynnus* (2.5 m (8 ft) long and 678 kg (1,496 lbs) in weight) and the black marlin *Istiompax indica* (4.6 m (15.3 ft) long and 750 kg (1,650 lbs) in weight) are some of the largest fish, and *Paedocypris progenetica* (9.7 mm (0.38 in) long) and the stout infantfish *Schindleria brevipinguis* (8.4 mm (0.33 in) long) are some of the smallest.

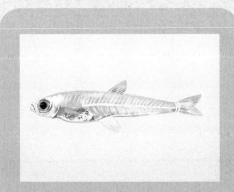

Paedocypris, *actual length: 9.7 mm (0.38 in)*

Atlantic bluefin tuna
Average length: 2.5 m (8 ft). Here shown at 5 percent of its actual size

Paedocypris progenetica would be the size of the dot on the letter "i" in comparison to this illustration of an Atlantic bluefin tuna

LEPIDOPTERA

FROM GREEK (LEPIS) "SCALE", + PTERON "WING"

Lepidoptera are insects characterized by the tiny silvery scales all over their bodies, which aid flight and offer a protective suit of armour. These scales allow for many decorative adaptations, making this one of the more colourful animal orders on Earth. Eye-spot patterns and vivid blues and reds feature commonly. Some moths, particularly, possess wing "tails" that may help their wearers avoid being eaten by bats. Lepidopterans are known for their caterpillar life-stage and the proboscis of the adult life-stage, a long, tongue-like structure that butterflies and moths use to acquire nectar. The order Lepidoptera includes more than 180,000 species, but there are likely to be many thousands more that scientists have not yet discovered.

1. LUNA MOTH
Sometimes called "moon moths", luna moths do not have mouths, but as caterpillars they like to eat hickory and walnut leaves. They live for approximately one week and females can lay up to 200 eggs in that time.

2. VIRGIN TIGER MOTH
These moths have excellent defences. They are able to make ultrasonic sounds to warn bats to stay away, and when gently squeezed they can produce a defensive chemical foam that smells and tastes terrible.

3. HIEROGLYPHIC MOTH
These moths are found in Central and North America as well as the Caribbean. They are called hieroglyphic moths because of the complicated pattern on their wings.

4. GREY HAIRSTREAK
One of the most common hairstreak butterflies in North America, they can be found ranging over nearly the entire continent. They visit and eat a huge variety of flowers and fruits.

Grey hairstreak

Bella moth

5. BELLA MOTH
The larval bella moths feed on plants that contain poisonous alkaloids. They keep these alkaloids in their bodies as they reach adulthood, then transfer them to their eggs, meaning that predators like ants and beetles will avoid them.

6. YELLOW GLASSY TIGER
The yellow glassy tiger flies slowly, and has been seen to glide in mid-air. The female will lay a single egg on the underside of a leaf which will hatch into a caterpillar in four days.

7. MONARCH BUTTERFLY
Monarch butterflies are famous for their annual migration where they cover thousands of miles. They were even taken to the International Space Station as caterpillars, and successfully grew to be adult butterflies.

8. COMMON SOOTYWING
While looking for a female, the male common sootywing will fly close to the ground in a zig-zag pattern. Caterpillars build shelters out of leaves, using their spinning silk.

9. SAPHO LONGWING
Sapho longwings have colourful, patterned wings which signal to predators that they are distasteful and possibly dangerous.

10. BLACK SWALLOWTAIL
The black swallowtail has developed a form of mimicry – they imitate another species to make themselves less likely to be fed on by a predator.

11. DANUBE CLOUDED YELLOW
The Danube clouded yellow butterfly is now quite rare, having declined over the last few decades. It can still be found in Romania where it lives on grasslands.

12. CECROPIA MOTH
The cecropia moth is the largest moth found in North America. It has a wingspan of 12–17 cm (5–7 in) wide. The male can detect pheromones produced by the female from 1.6 km (1 mile) away.

13. POPLAR HAWK MOTH

This very peculiar looking moth looks a lot like dead leaves of the poplar tree where it makes its home. It can be grey or a buff, brown colour.

14. ISABELLA TIGER MOTH

These larvae emerge from their eggs, become caterpillars, and freeze solid for the winter. In colder climates, summers are so short that the caterpillar must feed for several summers, freezing each winter before finally pupating.

15. GARDEN TIGER MOTH

The garden tiger moth's forewings are brown with a white pattern, and the hindwings are orange with a pattern of black dots. When disturbed, it will show its orange wings and fly off.

16. DRYAS IULIA

Also known as the Julia butterfly, this bright orange butterfly feeds on the nectar of flowers and the tears of the Caiman crocodile. The butterfly irritates the reptile's eyes to produce tears, then drinks them.

17. DEATH'S HEAD HAWKMOTH

The death's head hawkmoth gets its name from the skull-like marking on its thorax. These moths are able to squeak when disturbed, and can grow to have a wingspan of more than 13 cm (5 in).

18. AUTOMERIS IO MOTH

The male and female automeris io moths are extremely sexually dimorphic. Males are bright yellow, and females are reddish brown, though both have a big eye-spot on each hindwing.

19. RAJAH BROOKE'S BIRDWING

The male Rajah Brooke's birdwing butterfly can often be seen gathering at river banks and in mud puddles because they need to take in mineral-rich water.

Forest mother-of-pearl

20. FOREST MOTHER-OF-PEARL

So called because of their pink and purple iridescent hues, forest mother-of-pearl butterflies roost under leaves at night.

21. DELAWARE SKIPPER

Though named the Delaware skipper, this butterfly is fairly abundant in North America, and can be found in moist areas like marshes and bogs.

22. EMPEROR MOTH

The emperor moth can be found across Asia and Europe, including in the UK and Ireland. They have a false eye on both their forewings and their hindwings.

23. CINNABAR MOTH

The female cinnabar moth can lay up to 300 eggs, usually in batches of 30 or 60 on ragwort leaves. The caterpillars eat the poisonous plant and flowers as they grow.

24. BAORISA MOTH

This unique-looking moth is found in India and Southeast Asia, and is part of the Noctuidae family. Adult moths in this family have a tympanal organ that allows them to hear echolocation from bats which helps the moths to avoid them.

Long-tailed skipper

25. LONG-TAILED SKIPPER

Long-tailed skipper butterflies lay their eggs in stacks on the undersides of leaves. The caterpillars make nests out of leaves and stay inside them unless they are eating. They can also spit out a bright green liquid when disturbed!

26. COMMON BUCKEYE

The common buckeye has several large, black and purple false eyes across its fore- and hindwings. They migrate in huge numbers down through North America, overwintering in warmer southern states including Florida.

27. ZEBRA LONGWING

Zebra longwings roost in groups of up to 60 adults at night, for safety from predators. They are able to feed on pollen as well as nectar – this allows them to synthesize complex chemicals which make them toxic.

28. MORPHO PELEIDES

Like all butterflies, the morpho butterfly drinks their "food", rather than chewing it. As well as drinking fermenting fruit, nectar, or fungi, they are capable of sucking up the bodily fluids of dead animals.

29. DORCAS COPPER

Dorcas coppers lay their eggs on the undersides of leaves which drop to the ground during the autumn months. When they emerge in the spring, they must find their way back to the host plant to feed.

FIGURE 1. LEPIDOPTERA ANATOMY
Trogonoptera brookiana
(Rajah Brooke's birdwing)

Creatures of the order Lepidoptera evolved from primative insects in the Jurassic period. Though an incredibly diverse order, they all have two pairs of membranous wings, large compound eyes, and antennae.

Rajah Brooke's Birdwing

1. *Forewing*
2. *Thorax*
3. *Hindwing*
4. *Abdomen*
5. *Head*
6. *Antennae*

FIGURE 2. METAMORPHOSIS
Transition From Larvae to Adult

All Lepidoptera go through a caterpillar life-stage.

All butterflies and moths start their lives as eggs. The young larvae (caterpillars) hatch from eggs and eat the flowers or leaves of the specific host plant upon which they were laid.

Caterpillars moult as they grow, losing their old skins multiple times over a period of weeks or months. As soon as a caterpillar has reached its full size and weight, it is time for it to pupate. The caterpillar will attach itself to a twig or leaf (or sometimes make a silken hammock), then it will spin itself a cocoon (in the case of moths), or moult for a final time into a hard-shelled chrysalis (in the case of butterflies).

In this pupated state, the cells that make up the caterpillar's body pull apart and come back together again into a developing adult form, the butterfly or moth.

Transformation into a butterfly or moth is called holometabolism – commonly referred to as complete metamorphosis.

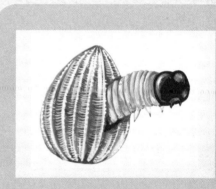

Monarch larva (caterpillar) *hatching from an egg.*

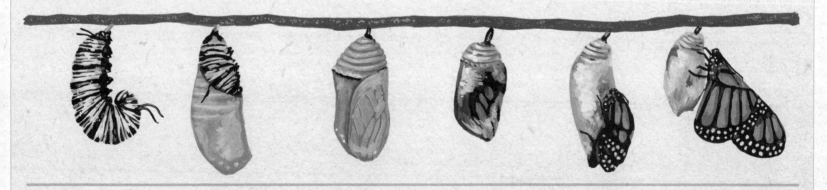

The **Monarch butterfly** *caterpillar forms a chrysalis and emerges as an adult butterfly.*

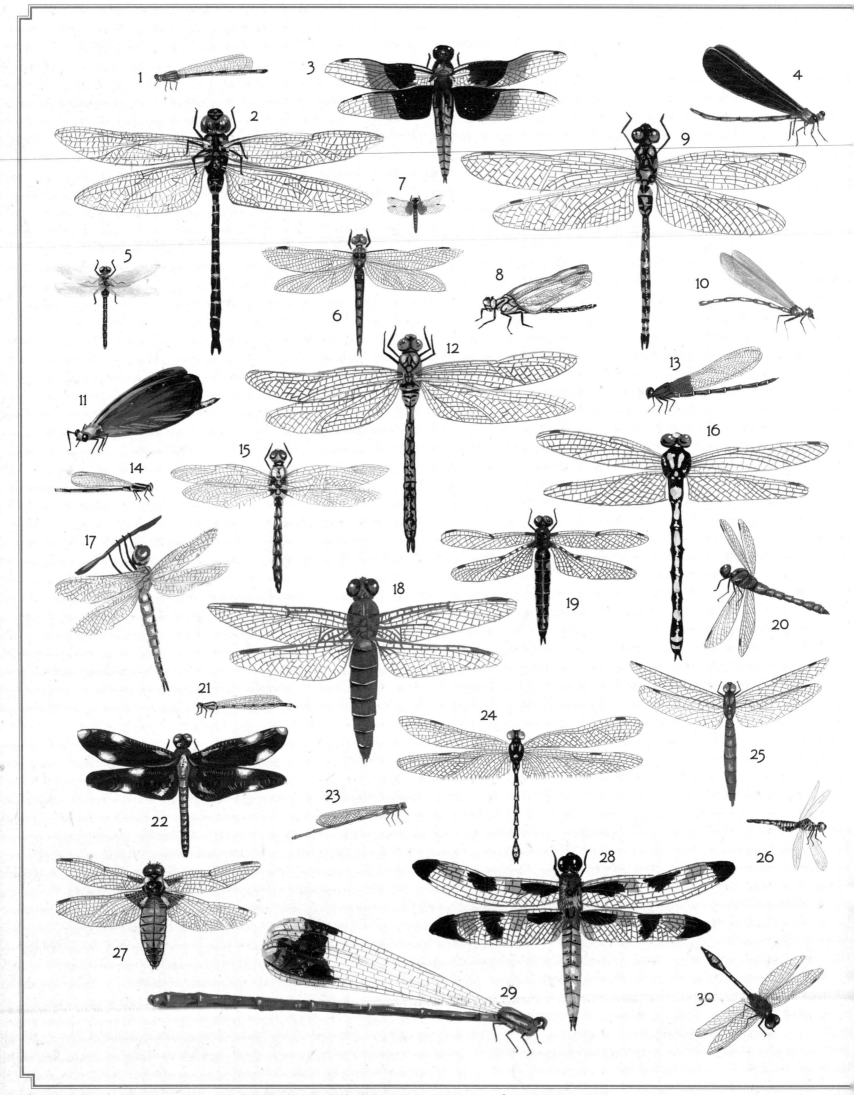

CREATURES OF THE ORDER | ODONATA

ODONATA

FROM ANCIENT GREEK ODONTOS "TOOTH"

Odonata is one of the most ancient insect orders on Earth. With two pairs of broad, powerful wings, Odonates are skilled hunters of other insects (particularly flies) which they catch in mid-air with the aid of highly-sensitive compound eyes and grasping legs. Within the order are two main groups: the damselflies (which lay their wings flat along their body at rest) and the dragonflies (whose wings rest outward). The largest living representative, a species of forest damselfly *Megaloprepus caerulatus*, has a wingspan of almost 20 cm (8 in) – as long as a human forearm. Individual Odonate species tell one another apart using a diverse array of colour patterns that may include garish reds, piercing yellows, and electric shades of blue.

Ischnura elegans

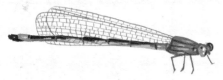

1. ISCHNURA ELEGANS
Female *Ischnura elegans*, or blue-tailed damselflies are not actually always blue-tailed! While mature females can be blue, they can also be olive green and brown, and younger ones can be pink, violet, or pale green.

2. REGAL DARNER
Unlike a lot of other male dragonflies, the male regal darners do not defend or patrol territories. They tend to fly close to vegetation to find their prey.

3. WIDOW SKIMMER
Widow skimmers can be found in muddy ponds, creeks, and streams in parts of North America. They catch their prey with their legs and then use their fierce mouthparts to bring it to their mouths.

4. EBONY JEWELWING
The solid black wings and green/blue iridescent body of the male ebony jewelwing make this damselfly stand out. Ebony jewelwings will stay at a good feeding area for hours or even days, and will defend the area from other damselflies.

5. RINGED BOGHAUNTER
Found in North American swamps and bogs, the ringed boghaunter dragonfly has a black/brown body ringed with orange bands. They are small dragonflies, growing to just over 33 mm (1.3 in) in length.

6. NORTHERN EMERALD
The northern emerald dragonfly is only found in small areas of the UK and Ireland. When they grow into their final adult stage, they leave the area and do not return to the bog or marsh until they are seeking a mate.

7. SCARLET DWARF
Sometimes called the tiny dragonfly, the scarlet dwarf is the smallest of the dragonflies with a wingspan of only 20 mm (0.7 in).

8. COMMON CLUBTAIL
This is the only species of dragonfly in the UK that has a space between its eyes. These yellow and black dragonflies are sexually dimorphic, with the female having a slightly larger abdomen and more rounded hindwings.

9. SOUTHERN HAWKER
The southern hawker is common throughout Europe. As nymphs, they feed on tadpoles, aquatic insects, and even small fish. As adults they catch various insects while in the air.

10. VARIABLE DANCER
The male variable dancer is thought to be the only violet-coloured damselfly. The "dancers", or Argia family, can be identified by their "bouncy" flight.

11. BEAUTIFUL DEMOISELLE
This damselfly can lay up to 300 eggs at a time, and unlike other Odonates, it can submerge itself underwater for short periods to do so.

12. EMPEROR DRAGONFLY
This brightly coloured dragonfly is the largest in the UK. The males very fiercely defend their territories, regularly patrolling up to 6 m (20 ft) above the water and rarely coming down to rest.

Emperor dragonfly

American rubyspot

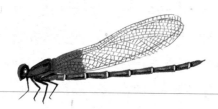

13. AMERICAN RUBYSPOT
Like some other damseflies, the female American rubyspot can submerge herself underwater for up to 60 minutes to lay her eggs.

14. ISCHNURA HETEROSTICTA
Also known as the common bluetail, this damselfly is found throughout the entire continent of Australia. The male has blue eyes, a blue thorax, and blue rings at the end of his tail.

15. TAU EMERALD
The tau emerald is a black and yellow dragonfly that reaches about 50 mm (2 in) in length. Both the male and the female have a rounded hindwing, making it difficult to tell which dragonfly is which.

16. PACIFIC SPIKETAIL
These large dragonflies can reach over 7.6 cm (3 in) in length. As nymphs, they lie buried in silt up to their eyes where they wait for prey.

17. GLOBE SKIMMER
The globe skimmer dragonfly is only 3.8 cm (1.5 in) long, but is able to fly 7,080 km (4,400 miles) without stopping, even across oceans. That's further than any other insect on Earth.

18. NEON SKIMMER
The male neon skimmer is a very distinctive, bright red dragonfly with amber-coloured wings. The female neon skimmer is paler, with clear wings.

19. DOT-WINGED BASKETTAIL
This dragonfly can be easily identified by the spots on the top of their hindwings. This is also where they get their name.

20. COMMON DARTER
Common darter dragonflies get their name from their hunting behaviour – they perch somewhere like a leaf or a gate, and then dart after the prey as they see it go by.

21. COMMON BLUE DAMSELFLY
The female common blue damselfly can either be blue or green. This is an aggressive species of damselfly, and the male will defend the female as they lay their eggs, both from damselflies and any other species.

22. SAPPHIRE FLUTTERER
You can tell which of these purple dragonflies is male and which is female by looking at their wings. Both have dark wings with clear patches, but the females have clear tips.

23. COMMON POND DAMSEL
This small orange damselfly has bright green eyes, and can be found in almost any type of freshwater habitat across most of Africa.

24. JAPANESE RELIC DRAGONFLY
This Japanese dragonfly lays its eggs on a plant above the water. When the eggs hatch, the nymphs will jump into the water below.

25. CRIMSON MARSH GLIDER
The crimson marsh glider is a part of the family Libellulidae, which is the largest family of dragonflies in the world. It can be found in ponds, marshes, and rivers in parts of Asia.

Crimson marsh glider

Grizzled pintail

26. GRIZZLED PINTAIL
This pintail *Acisoma panorpoides* is very small, reaching only 33 mm (1.29 in) in length. It is sometimes called the trumpet tail, because of the shape of its abdomen.

27. BROAD-BODIED CHASER
The broad-bodied chaser has a wide, flattened abdomen, making it appear fat! It is one of the most common dragonflies in Europe and central Asia.

28. TWELVE-SPOTTED SKIMMER
The twelve-spotted skimmer gets its name from the twelve spots on its wings. As it ages, it will also develop white spots.

29. GIANT HELICOPTER DAMSELFLY
This damselfly has the biggest wingspan of any living damselfly or dragonfly, at 19 cm (7.5 in). They eat web-building spiders, snatching them from their webs and perching somewhere to eat them.

30. RACKET-TAILED EMERALD
The racket-tailed emerald has a differently shaped abdomen to most emeralds. It is thinner, with a flat, spatula-like end.

FIGURE 1. SOUTHERN HAWKER DRAGONFLY ANATOMY
Aeshna cyanea

All members of the order Odonata have several things in common. They all have two sets of wings which they can move independently from one another, big eyes, and legs which they can use for grasping prey in mid-air.

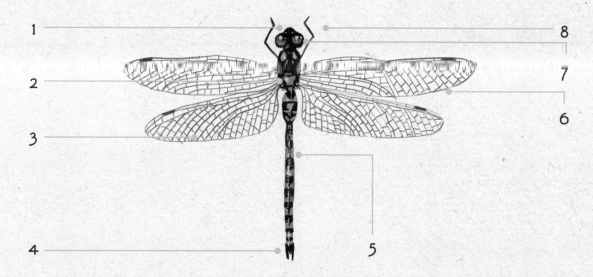

1. *Mandibles*
2. *Thorax*
3. *Hindwing*
4. *Anal appendage*
5. *Abdomen*
6. *Forewing*
7. *Large compound eyes*
8. *Legs*

FIGURE 2. NYMPH STAGE
Odonata life cycle

Dragonflies and damselflies will often mate while flying, locking together and flying in a joined pair while searching for suitable plants for egg laying. Sometimes, if a female cannot find a suitable plant, she will simply drop them into the water.

After days or weeks, the aquatic larvae (nymphs) hatch from these eggs. All members of the order Odonata have an aquatic nymph stage which feed on aquatic insects, as well as creatures as large as tadpoles and fish.

The nymphs themselves can experience up to fourteen moults where they grow and change before they reach their adult life stage. Sometimes this can take up to four years. When the conditions are right, it is at this point they climb out of the water and shed their outer skins before puffing out their wings. Now, as adults, they fly off in search of opportunities to reproduce, and the cycle continues.

Spotted skimmer *nymph*

Fully grown **spotted skimmer**

Odonata nymphs have a prehensile lower lip (called the mask) which is folded beneath their head. When they spot prey, it will shoot out at speed to grab them!

COLEOPTERA

FROM GREEK KOLEOS "SHEATH" + PTERON "WING"

Coleoptera is by far the most numerous and diverse of all insect orders on Earth. So far, scientists have discovered and named more than 400,000 Coleopterans from habitats all over the world. The secret to their success lies in their first set of wings (elytra) which offer protective body armour and can be pulled over the body to protect a second set of wings. This simple shell-like body plan has been co-opted for a host of specializations that allow for display, camouflage, and even swimming. Many Coleopterans, including the European stag beetle *Lucanus cervus*, display "sexual dimorphism" where males differ notably from females in form.

1. SCARLET LILY BEETLE

The scarlet lily beetle, as its name suggests, feeds on plants in the lily family. If these beetles sense danger, they are able to pretend to be dead as a defence mechanism, folding their arms and legs in, on their backs.

2. PINK SPOTTED LADY BEETLE

A female pink spotted lady beetle can lay up to 1,000 eggs. They feed on aphids, so eggs can usually be found wherever their prey live, though the larvae will travel up to 12 m (39 ft) to search for prey.

3. ASHY GREY LADY BEETLE

Though this lady beetle is not brightly coloured, when attacked it releases a toxin through its joints which makes it undesirable to predators.

4. PHOTURIS LUCICRESCENS

Like other species of the lightning bug genus *Photuris*, females are able to mimic the mating signals of other forms of firefly species. When they arrive to investigate, she eats them. This is called aggressive mimicry.

Phanaeus demon

5. PHANAEUS DEMON

The phanaeus demon is part of the scarab beetle family. It has a curved horn and a brightly coloured body, usually green with yellow reflections, green with gold reflections, and red with green reflections.

6. ONYMACRIS CANIDIPENNIS

This family of beetles have evolved to survive the challenging conditions of the desert in which they live. They "fog bask", where they climb to the top of a sand dune, and point their bottoms in the air. Water vapour from the fog condenses on the body, and runs down into the mouth.

7. BLUE FUNGUS BEETLE

The blue fungus beetle has a black body, and their elytra can range from a dull grey to a bright blueish-purple. The elytra are also covered in black indentations.

8. VIOLIN BEETLE

The violin beetle is named for its incredibly distinctive shape – the elytra and elongated head make it look just like a violin. It can grow up to 90 mm (3.5 in) in length.

9. FIVE-STRIPED FLEA BEETLE

The larvae of this beetle are reddish brown and covered in small nodules called balloon organs. It's possible that these organs are used for chemical communication.

10. 22-SPOT LADYBIRD

Though most ladybirds eat aphids, the 22-spot ladybird eats mildew. These beetles get their names, unsurprisingly, from the spots on their yellow backs.

11. GOLDEN SCARAB BEETLE

These brilliantly coloured beetles look almost like chunks of real gold. Their elytras' highly reflective sheen may have evolved to assist with camouflage or to dazzle would-be predators.

12. VARIED CARPET BEETLE

This tiny beetle only grows up to 3.5 mm (0.14 in) long. Larvae feed on dead insects and natural fibres like feathers and animal hair, and as adults they feed on pollen and nectar.

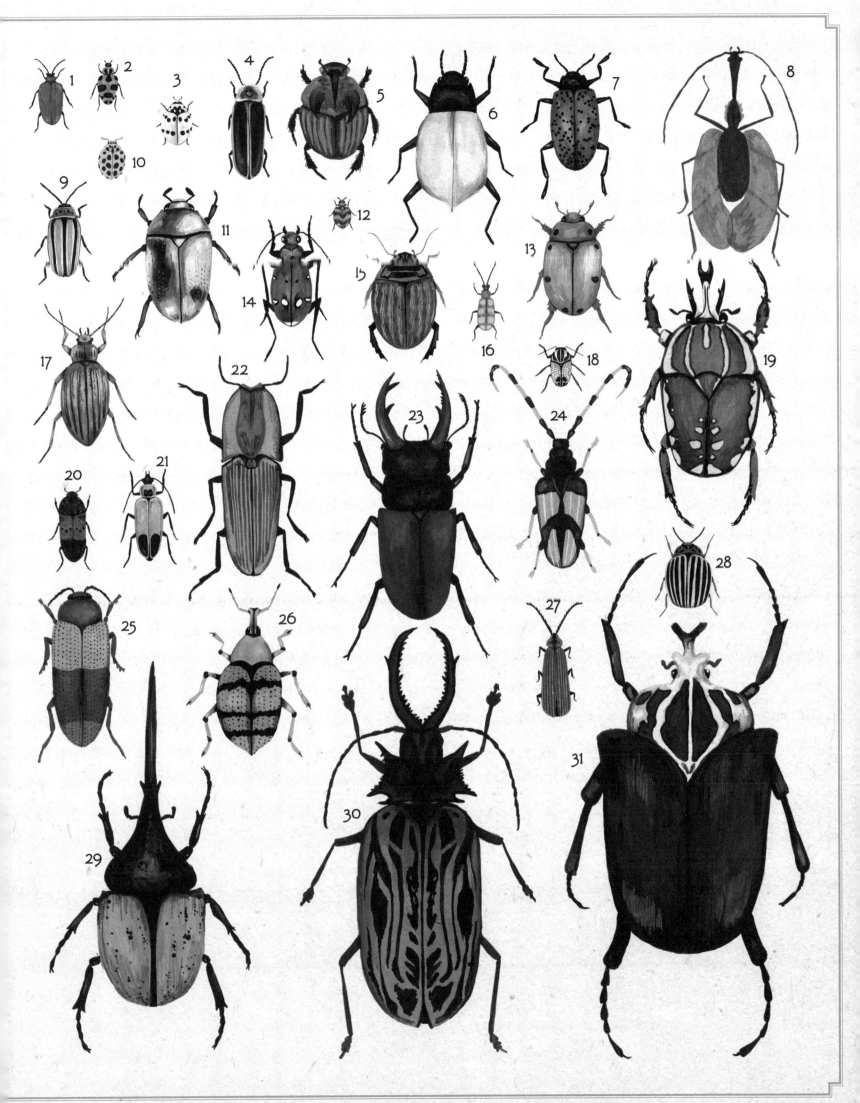

13. GRAPEVINE BEETLE

The grapevine beetle can be found across North America. It can reach around 2.5 cm (1 inch) long, and it eats fruits and leaves from grapevines.

14. GREEN TIGER BEETLE

Adult green tiger beetles are great predators. They have large eyes with excellent eyesight, strong, sickle-shaped jaws, and long legs that make them quick and agile.

15. LESSER DIVING BEETLE

These diving beetles actively pursue their prey, and they use their large mandibles to capture and devour them. They also have defensive glands that can secrete toxins to make them repellent to predators.

16. BANDED CUCUMBER BEETLE

The banded cucumber beetle has a red head and a green and yellow body and elytra. It can be found in North and South America, where it eats many kinds of fruits and vegetables.

17. GOLDEN GROUND BEETLE

The golden ground beetle has iridescent green elytra and head, and orange legs and antennae. These are predatory beetles that feed on worms, snails, and insects, subduing their prey in their mandibles before spraying them with a special digestive secretion.

18. CRYPTOCEPHALUS PSEUDOMACCUS

While *Cryptocephalus pseudomaccus* have elytra that has a shiny surface, most of the underside is covered with short and sparse whitish hairs.

19. GIANT AFRICAN FRUIT BEETLE

This large scarab beetle feeds on fruit and tree sap. The *Mecynorhina polyphemus* is often kept as a pet! The males can grow to 5 cm (2 in) long, and the males have antlers on their head.

20. LARDER BEETLE

The larder beetle is part of the skin beetle family and is a scavenger in both its larval and adult forms. In human habitations, these beetles forage for animal products like dried meat, skins and hides, or feathers, as well as some plant materials, like grain.

21. GOLDENROD SOLDIER BEETLE

These soldier beetles fly quickly, and with ease, sometimes being mistaken for wasps because of their yellow and black colouring. They feed on pollen, so are important pollinators for some flowering plants.

22. ARGENTINIAN CLICK BEETLE

Chalcolepidius limbatus is a type of "click beetle", which can make a loud clicking noise with its thorax that can also bounce the beetle into the air. It is found in Argentina, and can grow up to 3 cm (1.18 in) long.

23. EUROPEAN STAG BEETLE

This distinctive European beetle is famous for its huge, antler-like jaws. These are large beetles, with the male in the species reaching up to 7.5 cm (3 in) long. Male stag beetles will use their jaws to wrestle with each other over females or even food.

24. HORSE-BEAN LONGHORN

This longhorn beetle lays its eggs on many different host trees throughout the southern United States and Mexico. They are usually recognizable by their extremely long antennae.

Horse-bean longhorn

25. VARIABLE JEWEL BEETLE

This brilliantly coloured beetle has a green head and legs, and has yellow, dark blue, red, and green/blue bands on its elytra. It is a part of the jewel beetle family.

26. EUPHOLUS SCHOENHERRII

Part of the weevil family, *Eupholus schoenherrii* has bright blue legs with a metallic, blue-green elytra, covered in black bands. It can be found only in New Guinea.

27. RED SHOULDERED LYCID BEETLE

Unlike most beetles, the red shouldered lycid beetle has a soft elytra. They are brick red in colour, and are toxic to predators.

28. COLORADO POTATO BEETLE

Colorado potato beetles have bright orange, oval-shaped bodies with brown stripes. They are a serious pest of potatoes, and can bring serious damage to potato crops.

29. HERCULES BEETLE

The Hercules beetle is a species of rhinoceros beetle, and the male is famous for its long horn. This is one of the longest species of beetle in the world – the males can reach up to 17.5 cm (6.8 in) in length (including the horn).

30. SABRETOOTH LONGHORN BEETLE

Macrodontia cervicornis gets its common name from its large mandibles. This beetle spends most of its life in the larval stage, which can last up to 10 years. The adult phase of its life will only last a few months.

31. GOLIATH BEETLE

The goliath beetle is one of the largest (and heaviest) insects on Earth. These giants can be found in tropical forests in Africa, and eat high-sugar foods like tree sap and fruits.

FIGURE 1. SMALLEST TO LARGEST

Goliathus albosignatus
& *Ptenidium pusillum*

The order Coleoptera is one of the largest animal orders in existence. One quarter of all named animals are beetles. This hugely diverse order is made up of over 350,000 species of named beetle, almost certainly with many more that have yet to be discovered.

Beetles evolved from a primitive part of the insect family that first existed around 270 million years ago, and has since flourished and expanded to live all over the world in nearly every kind of habitat.

Some beetles, like the African goliath beetle *Goliathus albosignatus*, can reach more than 100 mm (4 in) in length. This makes the goliath beetle one of the largest insects on Earth, and it is said that it can lift a load that is more than 850 times heavier than its own body weight.

The smallest beetle on Earth is a representative of the Ptiliidae, or the featherwing beetle *Ptenidium pusillum*. Featherwings only grow up to 0.4 mm (0.015 in). They get their common name from their wings, which are mainly used for floating, like dandelion seeds.

Featherwing beetle enlarged. Maximum actual size of the featherwing 0.4 mm (0.015 in)

Maximum actual size of goliath beetle 11 cm (4.3 in)

FIGURE 2. COLEOPTERA ANATOMY

Mecynorhina polyphemus

Beetles do not have internal skeletons. Like all other insects (and other arthropods), they have an exoskeleton and, directly under the armour-like exoskeleton, there is a skin-like covering. The exoskeleton is made up of different plates, giving it flexibility.

Members of the order Coleoptera have a hardened pair of forewings (the elytra) which are not used in flight, but are lifted out of the way of the membranous hindwings. When they are resting, the membranous hind wings are folded away, protected, under the elytra.

Many male beetles have horns for fighting, and protecting their territories. The horns are sometimes even used as tools, for digging or manipulating materials to build nests.

Beetles also have claw-like hooks at the end of their six legs. In many species, including *Mecynorrhina polyphemu*, these hooks help them to climb trees to feed on tree sap and rotting fruit.

1. *Horns*
2. *Wing*
3. *Wing casing (elytra)*
4. *Antennae*

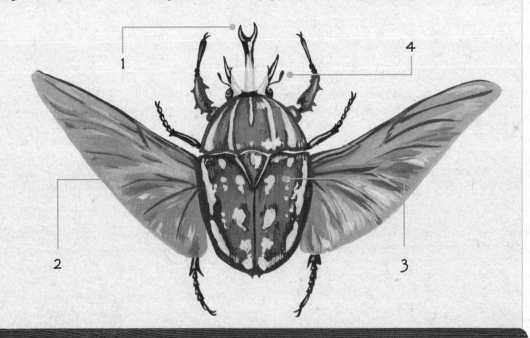

HYMENOPTERA

FROM GREEK HYMEN "MEMBRANE" + PTERON "WING"

Hymenopterans are insects whose females possess a needle-like tube (the ovipositor) which they use to squirt eggs into a variety of plants and even animals (on whom their larvae often live as parasites). In many species, particularly social wasps and bees, the ovipositor has been "hijacked" as a weapon to inject venom into potential predators. Some, like the tarantula hawk *Pepsis grossa,* are capable of immobilizing adult tarantulas with their venomous stingers, then dragging the paralyzed bodies to their nests to feed their babies. Venomous Hymenopterans may use lots of methods to warn potential predators of their stingers, most commonly the distinctive yellow-and-black "warning-stripes" that can be observed on many species.

1. GARDEN BUMBLEBEE
Bumblebees, unlike honey bees, do not lose their stingers after one sting, so they can sting attackers again and again. During summer months, these bees will work so hard that they sometimes die from exhaustion.

2. TRAP-JAW ANT
Trap-jaw ants have large mandibles that can open to 180 degrees. These mandibles are the fastest moving predatory appendages in the animal kingdom, and can snap shut at just 130 microseconds.

3. HORNFACED BEE
Hornfaced bees are effective pollinators that have been introduced into specific areas to increase pollination. A single bee can visit up to 2,500 flowers a day, spending about 4–8 minutes per flower collecting pollen and nectar, which they disperse as they go.

4. AUSTRALIAN HORNET
The Australian hornet is actually a member of the potter wasp species. Like other potter wasps, they are solitary and do not form colonies. The adults feed on nectar, and the larvae are fed caterpillars caught by the females.

European wool carder bee

5. EUROPEAN WOOL CARDER BEE
European wool carder bees get their name because they shave wool hair from the leaves of woolly plants (like the lamb's ear) to build their nests.

6. GIANT HORNTAIL
Female horntails use their ovipositors to dig into the dead or sick wood of pine trees and lay their eggs inside. The larvae live inside, developing for around three years.

7. THIEF ANT
Thief ants are so small that they often go unnoticed. They get their name because they frequently nest close to other ant species to steal their food.

8. BLACK GARDEN ANT
The black garden ants mate "on the wing". Like many ant species, the males and the virgin queens both have wings. When she has mated, the queen will land and burrow into the ground, laying eggs and starting her nest. This is the start of her colony.

Giant honey bee

9. GIANT HONEY BEE
The largest of the honey bees, the giant honey bee has an incredible defence mechanism against attacks from predators. They are able to heat themselves to around 45°C (113°F), and form a ball around the invader. The heat is lethal to the invading wasp or hornet and kills them.

10. ATANYCOLUS CAPPAERTI
Like most braconid wasps, this species is a parasitoid. They use their ovipositors to lay eggs inside the larval stages of other creatures like flies, butterflies, and some other insects. The wasp larvae feeds off the host and usually kills them when they emerge.

11. GREAT CARPENTER BEE
Carpenter bees build their nests inside pieces of dead wood. The female bees vibrate their bodies as they scrape their mandibles against the wood to do this. Typically, they have one entrance, but can have many tunnels.

Moss carder bee

12. MOSS CARDER BEE

Moss carder bees get their name from the way they make their hives. They build their nest on, or just under the ground, using moss and dried grass to cover it.

13. GREEN ORCHID BEE

These glossy, metallic green bees pollinate orchids. The male will collect different scented pollens in special pockets on his back legs and will release it to attract a female.

14. ASIAN GIANT HORNET

The Asian giant hornet is the world's largest hornet. They hunt other insects, and seem to favour honeybees. They are able to sting multiple times, but they kill honeybees by tearing them apart with their mandibles.

15. HONEYPOT ANT

These ants have special workers whose job it is to store energy-rich food supplies (honey), but instead of in their nest, they store it in their own bodies. When food is scarce, other ants will stroke their antennae, and they will regurgitate the stored food.

16. PSEUDOCHALCURA NIGROCYANEA

Eucharitid wasps, like *Pseudochalcura nigrocyanea,* are parasites. When they hatch from their eggs, the larvae will attach themselves to a passing ant. Once in the ant colony, they will prey on the ant larvae.

17. TARANTULA HAWK

The tarantula hawk is a spider wasp that hunts tarantulas. Its sting, which paralyzes the spider, is considered to be one of the most painful stings in the world.

18. BLUE MUD DAUBER

The blue mud dauber does not always have to build its nest, sometimes using a nest that has already been built. Mud daubers are the main predator of black widow spiders.

19. EASTERN YELLOW JACKET

As with many wasp and bee species, the queen eastern yellow jacket is the only member of her colony able to survive a winter. In early spring, she will find a suitable location and build a small new nest to start again.

20. GHOST ANT

The ghost ant has a black head, and a very pale or transparent abdomen and legs. These ants are difficult to see, as not only are they almost transparent, but they are very small, reaching only 1.5 mm (0.05 in) long.

21. TAWNY MINING BEE

The tawny mining bee digs holes in the ground to make its nests, leaving little volcano-like mounds. This is a solitary species of bee, and the females work alone to build the nests and feed the larvae.

22. EUROPEAN WASP

European wasps have been transported all over the world in cargo containers, and are a threat to indigenous wildlife where they have been introduced. They predate a wide variety of insects and spiders, and will compete with other animals in the area.

23. OAK GALL CHALCID

This wasp lays its eggs in oak trees. As the egg hatches and the larvae grows, it begins to secrete a material that makes the tissues of the tree grow around it, creating a special "safe-house" called a gall.

24. LARGE ROSE SAWFLY

The large rose sawfly feeds and lays its eggs on roses. When the female lays her eggs in rose stems, they "scar" the plant, leaving a long chain of holes which sometimes split apart along the middle.

25. WEAVER ANT

Weaver ants are famous for their amazing behaviour while constructing nests. They work together to bend leaves into different shapes, gluing them together with a papery white substance.

26. TURTLE ANT

The turtle ant has a distinctive, flat head, and has the ability to "parachute" – they can glide, directing their bodies back to their home tree if they happen to fall from higher branches.

27. ORIENTAL HORNET

This hornet is able to turn solar power into energy, becoming more active during the day when the sun is highest in the sky. The yellow stripe on its abdomen is coloured by the pigment, xanthopterin, which turns light into electrical energy.

28. LEAFCUTTER ANT

Leafcutter ants can be seen in their hundreds, transporting leaves back to their nest, but they are not eating the leaves, they are actually taking them underground to provide food for a fungus that they "farm" and then feed on.

29. ORCHARD MASON BEE

The orchard mason bee is well-loved by orchard farmers – a female can visit up to 60,000 flowers as she collects pollen and nectar preserves for her nest.

30. GREAT BLACK WASP

The great black wasp is so large that it is sometimes mistaken for a tarantula hawk wasp. These predators feed on insects like grasshoppers and sting their prey three times – once in the neck and twice in the thorax.

FIGURE 1. EUROPEAN WASP

Vespula germanica

All members of the order Hymenoptera have a distinctive body shape. A round head, a round thorax, and a big rounded abdomen.

The Hymenoptera undergo a complete metamorphosis from egg, to larvae, to adult, much like the Lepidoptera.

Some parts of the Hymenoptera family are incredibly social, living in large colonies, and some live solitary lives, only meeting to mate. In social colonies, the queen will create armies of sterile workers that will help her "royal" offspring to thrive.

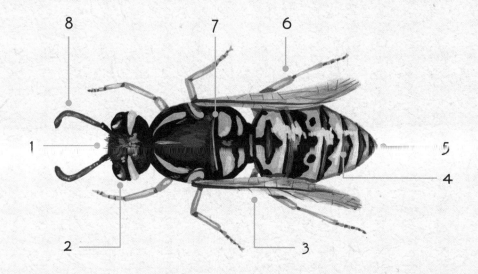

1. *Head*
2. *Compound eyes*
3. *Wing*
4. *Abdomen*
5. *Stinger/ovipositor*
6. *Legs*
7. *Thorax*
8. *Antennae*

FIGURE 2. OVIPOSITOR

Atanycolus cappaerti

Often, in the order Hymenoptera, the female will have a tube through which eggs can be squirted into things, like wood, fruit, or even caterpillars! Ovipositors can be used to prepare a place for the egg, transmit the egg, and properly place it.

Some wasps are able to use their long, thin ovipositor to dig into the wood of trees – first listening for the vibrations made by a host larvae or insect, then drilling through to place their eggs.

In many hymenopterans, the ovipositor has been modified into a sting. The added venomous aspect allows the insect to lay eggs without the risk of injury from the intended host.

Braconid wasps even inject the host with a virus that suppresses the immune system to allow the larvae to grow undetected.

1. *Head*
2. *Wings*
3. *Abdomen*
4. *Stinger/ovipositor*

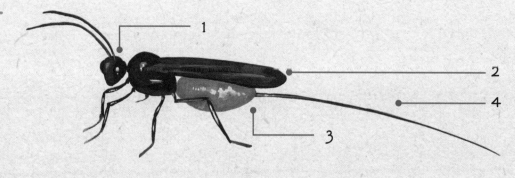

Braconid wasp

SQUAMATA

FROM LATIN SQUAMA "SCALE"

The order Squamata (or scaled reptiles) are masters of survival. With tough, scaly skin that protects them from water loss in dry environments, they have come to colonize the most arid and scorching landscapes on Earth. Divided neatly into snakes and lizards, squamates share a simple back-boned (vertebrate) body plan as well as possessing strong jaws capable, in the case of snakes, of almost completely dislocating when swallowing larger prey items. In all, there are more than 10,000 representatives of this ancient order. Each is dependent on the sun to provide heat for its metabolism. Only a handful of species, such as the adder *Vipera berus*, have adapted to life in colder climates.

Iberian worm lizard

1. IBERIAN WORM LIZARD

Like many lizards, the Iberian worm lizard will use the rocks in its habitat to warm or cool itself to the correct body temperature. To stay cool they dig, burrowing up to 10 cm (4 in) into the soil.

2. YELLOW ANACONDA

This constrictor is one of the largest snakes in the world, growing to an average of 4 m (13 ft) in length. As predators, they forage in shallow water and hunt birds, fish, lizards, mammals, and more.

3. GRANITE NIGHT LIZARD

The granite night lizard changes the colour of its skin from day to night. In its "dark phase" during the day, it is dark brown and white, and during its "light phase" at night, it is white with irregular spots on its back and tail.

4. TOKAY GECKO

Tokay geckos are found throughout Asia. Their native habitat is the rainforest, though they have adapted to human homes, climbing walls and ceilings to look for insects.

5. ARUBAN WHIPTAIL

These distinctive lizards are found on the island of Aruba. Their dark bodies are covered in bright turquoise spots, with turquoise bands down their tails.

6. WESTERN SKINK

Western skinks flee if threatened, but if they are caught by a predator they can detach their tail as a distraction. As with many lizards, the tail will eventually grow back, but may be a different colour and shape.

7. SUNBEAM SNAKE

Sunbeam snakes are known for their highly iridescent scales. Their unusual scale patterns scatter light, exposing an array of colours across their body when dazzled by the sun.

8. CHECKERBOARD WORM LIZARD

Checkerboard worm lizards lack legs and instead have loose skin which they use in an accordion-like movement for locomotion. They spend most of their lives underground, so they only have rudimentary eyes and poor eyesight.

9. HOLASPIS GUENTHERI

Holaspis guentheri, also known as the neon blue-tailed tree lizard, is arboreal. They live in trees and have light skeletons, packed full of air pockets, making them capable of gliding up to 30 m (100 ft).

10. COMMON EUROPEAN ADDER

The European adder (also known as the European viper) is a variable coloured snake with a distinctive "lightning bolt" pattern. It is the only snake that lives within the Arctic circle.

11. GILA MONSTER

The Gila monster is one of the only venomous lizards in the world. Its venom is a mild neurotoxin. These lizards are able to latch onto their victims and chew, which allows neurotoxins to move through grooves in their teeth and into the open wound.

Gila monster

12. IBERIAN ROCK LIZARD

The Iberian rock lizard's tail can be almost twice the length of its body. Males that have lost their tails to predators have a lower status within the dominance hierarchy and generally court fewer females. Females without tails are also less frequently courted.

13. BRAHMINY BLIND SNAKE

Brahminy blind snakes are non-venomous, and are completely fossorial – burrowing animals. They are almost blind, only registering light, and are sometimes mistaken for earthworms.

14. BAWENG SATANIC LEAF GECKO

Found on the island of Madagascar, the Baweng satanic leaf gecko has a flat tail that mimics a decaying leaf. During daylight hours, these adaptations help the gecko blend into its surroundings.

15. REGAL HORNED LIZARD

The regal horned lizard is a small, flat lizard about the size of a human's palm, with spikes all over its body. Despite the spikes, it usually tries to flee, and its main defence is the ability to squirt blood from its eyes.

16. GALAPAGOS PINK LAND IGUANA

This critically endangered iguana is pink with dark markings along its body. These lizards are primarily herbivores, feeding on prickly pear leaves and fruit.

17. GREEN TREE PYTHON

Green tree pythons are arboreal (tree dwelling) and nocturnal, making this species difficult to find in the wild. While resting in the branches of trees the python will loop its tail around in a coil over the branches and place its head in the middle.

Banded sea krait

18. BANDED SEA KRAIT

This venomous sea snake is found in tropical Indo-Pacific oceanic waters. They have a specially adapted, paddle-like tail, and they spend much of their time underwater. They return to land to digest their food and rest, and can only move at around a fifth of their swimming speed.

19. SLOW WORM

Despite their name and appearance, slow worms are neither worms nor snakes, but are in fact limbless lizards. They may be the longest-living lizards on Earth – they can live up to 30 years in the wild and at least 54 in captivity.

20. ROCK MONITOR

The rock monitor is Africa's second longest lizard at up to 1.5 m (5 ft). They are almost entirely carnivorous, feeding on invertebrates as juveniles and vertebrates as adults.

21. MEXICAN MOLE LIZARD

The soft-scale patterns on the mole lizard's skin give a corrugated appearance like that of a worm. These highly effective diggers have a genus all to themselves, the Bipes. They have two legs just behind the head, and a snake-like body that trails behind them.

22. LANGAHA MADAGASCARIENSIS

The Malagasy leaf-nosed snake is an arboreal species found on the island of Madagascar. Their strange nasal appendage (pointy in the male, leaf-shaped in the female) helps them blend in with vines and branches as they stalk and ambush their prey.

23. CHINESE CROCODILE LIZARD

The Chinese crocodile lizard is named for the appearance of its tail, which has an enlarged pair of scales running in two sharply protruding ridges down its length, much like a crocodile's tail.

24. VEILED CHAMELEON

These chameleons have a colour changing ability that is affected by many things, including their mood, the temperature, and their overall health.

25. INDIAN COBRA

Indian cobras are easily identified by their large and quite impressive hoods, which they expand when feeling threatened. Most Indian cobras also have the famous, spectacle-shaped mark on the back of their hoods.

26. AUGRABIES FLAT LIZARD

The brightly coloured augrabies (or broadley's) flat lizard is a species of flat lizard. They are able to make impressive leaps, a technique they put to good use in catching black flies as they swarm overhead.

27. GREEN VINE SNAKE

Green vine snakes have binocular vision, like humans, which helps them to identify and track their prey. They are venomous, and their toxic saliva renders their prey immobile.

28. CAROLINA ANOLE

The Carolina anole is bright green, but can quickly change colour to brown, yellow, or grey depending on its mood, temperature, and humidity. Though it shares this similarity with chameleons, the Carolina anole represents a different part of the lizard family.

29. THORNY DRAGON

Thorny dragons only eat ants and can consume thousands of small, black ants a day. They collect moisture on their bodies during the night through condensation, which is then channelled down towards their mouths to drink.

30. FRILLED-NECK LIZARD

The Australian frilled lizard has a large ruff of skin that is usually folded against its neck. When it feels threatened, the lizard rises up on its hind legs, opens its mouth, and unfurls the colourful, pleated skin flaps that encircle its head, all while hissing.

FIGURE 1. SCALES AND SHIELDS
Skin in the order Squamata

The Squamata evolved from a very early branch of reptiles during the mid-Jurassic period. They are the largest order of scaled reptiles, and they are distinguished by their skin, which is made up of either horny scales or shields.

Snakes are entirely covered in scales of different shapes and sizes. A snake's scales protect its body, helps it to move and give the snake its colours and patterns, which it uses for camouflage and anti-predator displays. Except for on their heads, snake scales overlap, like the tiles on the roof of a house. They have different types of scales on their head, body, and tail.

Lizard scales are made of horny skin, and many have bony plates underneath them named osteoderms. They are sometimes overlapping, sometimes pointy, and sometimes plate-like.

Creatures of the order Squamata will regularly moult and replace their skin. This allows them to get rid of the old, worn skin (which may be dry, or have marks from injury), and to rid themselves of parasitic mites and ticks.

Most lizards lose their skin periodically, with it coming off in flakes. Snakes, and a few lizards, lose the skin from their body in one long piece. The old skin will break near the mouth, and they will wriggle out of it, sometimes helped by rubbing against rough surfaces, like rocks.

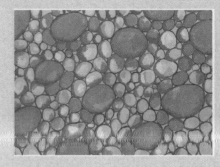

Tokay gecko skin

King cobra, shedding its skin.

FIGURE 2. ANATOMY
Lizard and snake

There are some features that all lizards and snakes have in common – a vertebrate skeleton comprising a spine, two pairs of legs, and a jaw that opens up and down. Some members of this family, the legless lizards and snakes, have lost their limbs over time.

When lizards move, they move their four limbs. Snakes move by using their muscles and scales. Groups of legless lizards, like the slow worms, can only move using a side-to-side motion, almost as though they are still using the four legs that they have lost.

Snakes and legless lizards can be told apart by more than the way they move – snakes don't have ears or eyelids that they can shut, but lizards do.

Snakes have long bodies and short tails, legless lizards have short bodies and long tails. When stuck or caught by predators, many lizards have the ability to detach their tails and escape, and legless lizards have this too. This is called autotomy – they are able to grow their tails back over time, but it can take a few years, and they may only be able to do it once.

Rock monitor

Common European adder

CREATURES OF THE ORDER | TESTUDINES

TESTUDINES

FROM LATIN TESTA "SHELL"

Testudines have unusual fused ribcages which provide the architecture for a charismatic protective shell. The order includes more than 300 living species of turtles, tortoises, and terrapins, all of whom have a keratin beak not unlike that of birds. Testudines also lay shelled eggs, often buried in specially dug burrows. Many species can be told apart by the bony scales (scutes) that form the external armour of the shell. The specific arrangements of these scutes allow some species greater flexibility in movement or enhanced protection, if needed, depending on their habitat. In the Eastern shiny softshell *Apalone spinifera* and the leatherback turtle *Dermochelys coriacea* these scutes have been replaced with leathery skin.

1. MADAGASCAN BIG-HEADED TURTLE

This critically endangered turtle is one of the most threatened turtles in the world. It lives in the rivers and lakes of Madagascar, and has, as the name suggests, a very large head.

2. DIAMONDBACK TERRAPIN

This small terrapin is well-adapted for eating crabs, mussels, clams, and sea snails. It can also eat fish, insects, and carrion (dead animal flesh).

3. BLACK-BREASTED LEAF TURTLE

This turtle has a hook on its upper jaw which is uses to help it to climb. Its shell is orange-brown and it has wide, protuberant (bulging) eyes.

4. GOPHER TORTOISE

Gopher tortoises are known for their digging ability. Using their shovel-like front legs, they dig burrows up to 14.5 m (48 ft) long, and 3 m (10 ft) underground. These burrows protect them from the sun, wind, and cold.

5. ANGONOKA TORTOISE

The angonoka tortoise is critically endangered, with fewer than 1,000 thought to be left in the wild. Conservation efforts for these tortoises are difficult, as females only begin breeding at the ages of 10–15 years old.

6. COMMON PADLOPER

The common padloper spends a lot of its life hiding under rocks and foliage for cover. It is a small tortoise, with an average length of 110 mm (4.3 in), and is often preyed on by birds, baboons, dogs, and other predators.

7. ORNATE BOX TURTLE

The ornate box turtle's plastron is hinged, and can be completely closed against its carapace, allowing the turtle to withdraw its head and enclose itself in a protective "box".

8. YELLOW-BLOTCHED MAP TURTLE

The male yellow-blotched map turtle has yellow blotches covering most of its shell along with light cream and black colour patterns. The black markings fade as they age, so the patterns are useful in knowing how old the turtle is.

Blanding's turtle

9. BLANDING'S TURTLE

The Blanding's turtle has a dark green carapace and body, but has a distinctive bright yellow throat and chin, which can be seen from a distance. Unlike most turtles, they can hibernate underwater.

10. PANCAKE TORTOISE

The pancake tortoise is named for its flat, unusually thin, and flexible shell. These tortoises are fast, agile climbers, and can use this skill (as well as their flat bodies) to escape into rock crevices when threatened.

11. MATA MATA

This unique looking turtle is the only existing species in the Chelus genus. They are large turtles with flat, triangular-shaped heads, and they have a long "horn" on their beak. Their carapaces resemble bark and fallen leaves, and are useful for camouflage.

12. LEATHERBACK SEA TURTLE

The leatherback sea turtle is the largest of all living turtles, reaching up to 2.2 m (7.2 ft) long. It is a soft-shelled turtle, and its carapace is made of skin and oily flesh.

13. SCORPION MUD TURTLE

The scorpion mud turtle can sometimes burrow into mud or piles of dry leaves during times of drought, and live in a semi-dormant state, a bit like hibernation.

14. SPOTTED TURTLE

Spotted turtles can live for more than 100 years, and are completely covered in yellow spots. You can tell the sex by the colour of their chins; the male has a black chin and the female has a bright orange or yellow chin.

15. PAINTED TURTLE

Painted turtles have split into four different subspecies in North America. The southern painted turtle (pictured), is the smallest subspecies, with a red stripe on its shell and a tan underbelly.

16. HAWKSBILL SEA TURTLE

Hawksbill sea turtles have beautifully patterned shells and are important to the conservation of coral reefs. They eat sea sponges, and by removing them allow the coral to grow.

17. SPINY TURTLE

The spiny turtle has a distinctive shell with a spiked edge that acts as a deterrent to predators like snakes. Unfortunately, the spikes can get worn down with age, removing that protection.

18. COMMON BOX TURTLE

The common box turtle will eat almost anything, including plants, insects, and even roadkill. They often eat poisonous mushrooms, which doesn't kill them, but makes their flesh deadly to predators.

Big-headed turtle

19. BIG-HEADED TURTLE

Just like you might expect from its name, the big-headed turtle's head is so huge that it can't pull it into its shell for protection, but instead has powerful jaws to defend itself.

20. COMMON MUSK TURTLE

These turtles are sometimes called stinkpot turtles, because they can secrete a smelly substance (sometimes described as smelling like burnt food) as a deterrent to predators.

21. FLORIDA REDBELLY TURTLE

To keep its eggs safe, the Florida redbelly turtle often lays them in alligator nests. This way, the alligators think the eggs are theirs and protect them against predators.

22. EASTERN SPINY SOFTSHELL

Unlike most turtles, the eastern spiny softshell has a soft, leathery shell. It spends most of its life lying in the mud at the bottom of rivers, hiding from predators and catching prey.

23. GOLDEN COIN TURTLE

This turtle's distinctive yellow stripes make it one of the prettiest turtles in the world. Sadly, it is also one of the rarest, with humans hunting it for food, medicine, or to keep as a pet.

24. CENTRAL AMERICAN RIVER TURTLE

The Central American river turtle is protected by many laws and international agreements, as it is critically endangered due to hunting by humans.

25. EASTERN LONG-NECKED TURTLE

Also known as the snake-necked turtle, this turtle uses its long neck to snatch up prey. When threatened, it can release a very smelly chemical to warn off predators.

26. GALAPAGOS TORTOISE

This tortoise, which only lives in the Galapagos Islands in Ecuador, is the longest-living and biggest tortoise in the world, growing to over 1.5 m (5 ft) long and living for up to 150 years!

27. COMMON SNAPPING TURTLE

This huge turtle is one of the last surviving representatives of a once-great family of snapping turtles that even lived alongside the dinosaurs.

28. CHINESE POND TURTLE

The tiny Chinese pond turtle is small enough to fit in your hand. Despite living in water, they are weak swimmers and stick to slow-moving or swampy water.

29. RED-FOOTED TORTOISE

This common tortoise is an amazing survivalist. In cold weather, it can slow down its metabolism so it barely needs to eat. It can survive for a month on as little as a single banana.

30. INDIAN STAR TORTOISE

The Indian star tortoise's amazing, star-patterned shell is rounder than most other tortoises, meaning that it can easily get back on its feet if it is tipped onto its back.

FIGURE 1. ANATOMY

Testudines

The creatures of the order Testudines are chiefly categorised by their bony or cartilaginous shell.

The shell of a member of the Testudines family develops from the ribs of the creature and acts as a shield. The upper shell is called the carapace, and the lower shell is called the plastron. A turtle cannot crawl out of its shell – the inside of its shell is made up of around 60 bones, including both the ribs and backbone.

Most turtles, terrapins, and tortoises are all able to retract their necks as a defence mechanism, though not all the same way. Some pull their necks back under the spine, and some pull them to the side.

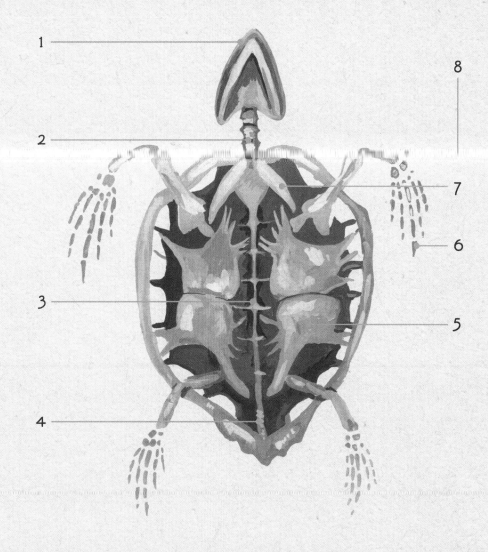

1. *Mandible*
2. *Neck vertebrae*
3. *Thoracic vertebrae*
4. *Tail vertebrae*
5. *Plastron*
6. *Phalanges*
7. *Scapula*
8. *Carpals*

FIGURE 2. TURTLE LIFE CYCLE

Birth, hatching, and return to the water

Turtles, terrapins, and tortoises can live a long time, with even the smallest living up to 30–40 years, and some larger species regularly living more than 100 years. Some species, like the loggerhead turtle, may live 30 years before reaching adulthood and becoming ready to lay their eggs.

Turtles always return to the place of their birth to look for a mate, and a female will use the same beach that she was born on to lay her eggs, as she already knows it is a good, habitable area for her babies. Females continue to mate until all of their clutches of eggs are fertilized, and each may lay up to eight clutches of eggs over a period of a few weeks. Female turtles do not return to breed again every year, but the males do.

Female turtles dig holes in the ground, then lay their eggs inside before covering them up. The baby turtles then have to break out of their eggs and come up through the sand or soil, then immediately head for water. Turtles are left to fend for themselves immediately from birth, and this is a dangerous time for them, as they must avoid any predators.

Hawksbill sea turtle

ANURA

FROM GREEK AN "WITHOUT" + OURA "TAIL"

Anurans (tailless amphibians) can be divided into two basic groups, broadly referred to as frogs and toads. Frogs often have smooth skin and live in wetlands. Toads often (but not always) have dry, warty skin and colonise drier regions, including grasslands and temperate forests. Both families are characterised by their shell-less eggs in which tadpoles develop before metamorphosis into adult form. Some species, including the midwife toad Alytes obstetricans tend to their eggs away from water, keeping them moist whilst wrapped up around their hind-legs. Unlike other amphibians, Anurans depend heavily on noises (including croaks, chirps, and squeaks) during their breeding seasons.

Emei moustache toad

1. EMEI MOUSTACHE TOAD

During the breeding season, *Leptobrachium boringii* will grow sharp spines on their upper lips (like a moustache) specifically to spike rivals males with. They will sometimes drive off other males and take over their nest sites, including any eggs they may have already had.

2. SPINY COCHRAN FROG

Unlike other members of the order Anura, the female will lay her eggs on the underside of plants that hang over streams. When the tadpoles hatch from their eggs, they fall into the stream.

3. COMMON MIDWIFE TOAD

The female common midwife toad will lay her eggs in a string formation, and the male will wrap them around his body. He then carries them around until their development is complete and he seeks out a cool pool where the tadpoles can be released.

4. STRAWBERRY POISON DART FROG

Strawberry poison dart frogs provide dual parental care to their offspring. The male frogs defend and water the nest, and the females feed the tadpoles.

5. JAPANESE COMMON TOAD

This toad is native to Japan, and like many toads, hibernates during the winter, digging underground, deeply into the soil below the frostline.

6. COSTA RICA VARIABLE HARLEQUIN TOAD

Sometimes called the clown frog, until recently, this toad was thought to have been extinct, but a small breeding population was found in a mountainous reserve in Costa Rica.

7. MALAGASY RAINBOW FROG

These frogs are very colourful. They breed in temporary pools, and eggs develop quickly to adulthood, in only 4–8 weeks. It is thought that this is to avoid them being washed away in heavy rains and flash floods.

8. WALLACE'S FLYING FROG

These frogs have developed membranes of skin between their long fingers and toes. They live in trees, and leap from branch to branch. When threatened, they can leap from trees and splay their fingers and toes to glide safely.

9. CANE TOAD

The cane toad has poison glands which make them incredibly toxic to most animals if they eat them. They breed in huge amounts, sometimes laying thousands of eggs in a single clump.

10. BLUE POISON DART FROG

Unlike in most animal families, it is the female blue poison dart frogs that fight over the male for mating. Once the female has won, she will lay her eggs, and the male will fertilise them.

11. MEXICAN BURROWING TOAD

The only species in the genus Rhinophrynus, this toad is extremely different from all other amphibian species. They are fossorial, spending nearly all of their time burrowing undergound and only coming up during heavy rains and to mate.

12. TOMATO FROG

When threatened, a tomato frog will puff up its body and secrete a thick, sticky substance. This acts as a deterrent to predators, often even causing the predator to drop the frog.

13. AFRICAN CLAWED FROG

These frogs gets their name from the three short claws on each of their hind legs. They use these claws to shred things like fish or tadpoles before using their forelegs to shove the pieces into their mouths.

14. ORIENTAL FIRE-BELLIED TOAD

If threatened, the oriental fire-bellied toad will sometimes flip itself over onto its back to show potential predators its bright red and black underside, warning them of its toxicity.

15. PEBBLE TOAD

Pebble toads have a fairly unique defence mechanism, pulling their arms and legs under their body, and tucking their head in, therefore resembling a pebble! If they are on a slope, then they will roll down, escaping the predator.

16. COMMON SURINAME TOAD

These toads mate in a unique way. The female will lay her eggs, and the male will embed them into her back where they sink into her skin and form pockets. Once the baby toads have been "born" from her back the mother will shed the thick skin used for the implantation and start again.

17. TURTLE FROG

Unlike most burrowing frogs and toads, it is the turtle frog's front legs that are strong and muscular. This frog eats termites, so its strong frong legs also help them access termite nests.

18. PURPLE FROG

Sometimes called the pig-nosed frog (because of its white, protruding snout), *Nasikabatrachus sahyadrensis* spends much of its life lying dormant beneath the ground. They emerge to breed during the Indian monsoon season.

19. RED-EYED TREE FROG

This aboreal frog is easily recognisable by its red eyes and blue inner-legs. They are not poisonous, but their bright colouring may startle would-be predators.

20. VIETNAMESE MOSSY FROG

The Vietnamese mossy frog has brown and green mottled skin, very closely resembling a moss-covered rock. It is a highly effective form of camouflage.

21. PANAMANIAN GOLDEN FROG

This frog is critically endangered due to habitat destruction. They inhabit noisy, fast-moving streams. Because of the noise, they communicate by signalling – males often wave their arms to get attention from females.

22. DESERT RAIN FROG

The desert rain frog is very small and round and has a very unusual, high-pitched, scream-like cry. They are nocturnal, burrowing in the sand in the mornings and emerging to hunt insects at night.

23. TROSCHEL'S TREE FROG

This tree frog lives in sub-tropical forests in South America. It is easily recognisable by its orange-brown body with black and white striped sides.

24. COMMON TOAD

Common toads live far away from water (unless they are mating) in shallow burrows. They forage for prey, like insects, spiders, worms, and slugs, and usually walk, not hop.

Common toad

25. DARWIN'S FROG

Once tadpoles start to wriggle in their eggs, the male will pick up the eggs with his tongue and push them through his mouth into the vocal sack. While inside the male, the tadpoles hatch and develop into frogs. Once they are around 1 cm (0.4 in) long, they are released from the male's mouth.

26. GOLIATH FROG

The goliath frog is the largest living frog, reaching 32 cm (12.6 in) long. They can weigh up to 3.2 kg (7 lbs), and can leap more than 3 m (10 ft) in a single jump.

27. ARGENTINE HORNED FROG

These horned frogs are ambush hunters, remaining motionless and waiting for prey to pass by. They will try and eat anything that passes nearby, sometimes even attempting to eat things they cannot fit into their mouths.

28. AMERICAN BULLFROG

The American bullfrog is extremely territorial, with dominant males wrestling over territory and females. They are ambush predators and will eat birds, fish, snakes, mice, and insects – basically anything they can fit into their mouths.

29. GOLDEN MANTELLA FROG

This small frog reaches 25.4 mm (1 in) in length. They have either red, yellow, or golden-orange skin, and short legs with sticky discs on the end of their fingers.

30. MARBLED REED FROG

These frogs can display different colours and patterns on their skin during the day and night. During the night, they are generally more brightly coloured with brilliant patterns.

FIGURE 1. TOADS VS. FROGS
Similarities and Differences

Around 88 percent of amphibians are classified as a member of the order Anura, the frogs. Technically, toads are small part of this frog "family" that have adapted to more of a life on land. Most frogs have moist skin and are more likely to be found in damp habitats near water, and their legs are often long and adapted for jumping. Generally, toads have thicker, warty skin and are able to live in drier habitats than frogs. They lay spawn in strings and often possess poison glands.

Red-eyed tree frog

Cane toad

FIGURE 2. ANURA LIFE CYCLE
Tadpoles to adults

Frogs and toads breed during the spring. First, the female will lay her eggs (usually in water) and the male will fertilise them. The amount of eggs laid varies from species to species, and they are either laid in clusters or clumps (called a mass), or in long chains (toads usually lay their eggs like this).

The eggs will hatch into tadpoles, which have gills and a tail, and breathe underwater (the time this takes varies from species to species). They spend their time swimming in the water, eating, and growing. Their back legs develop and their eyes become more adult-like. Their front legs then develop and their tail re-absorbs into their body. Finally, at metamorphosis, they breathe air with their lungs, and their tail has shrunk completely.

They leave the pond as froglets or toadlets, ready for life on land.

Frogspawn (a mass)

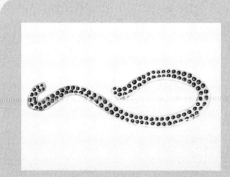

Toadspawn (chains)

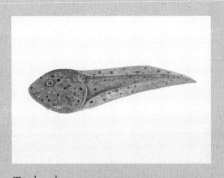

Tadpole

Tadpole with legs

American bullfrog

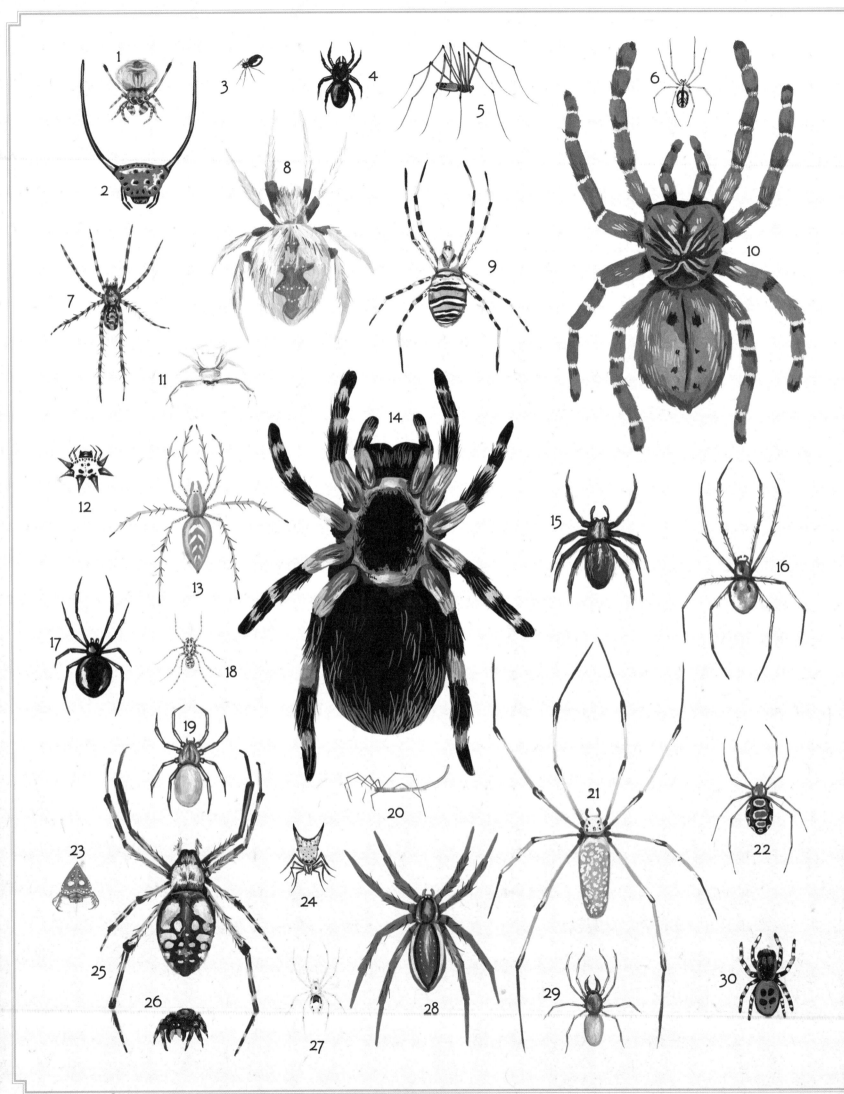

CREATURES OF THE ORDER | ARANEAE

ARANEAE

FROM LATIN ARĀNEUS "SPIDER, SPIDERWEB" + EAE "ORDER"

With more than 45,000 species, nearly all representatives of the Araneae (spiders) are specialist hunters of insects and other invertebrates. It is estimated that this order consumes 600 million tonnes of insects each year. The success of Araneae lies in their sharp senses, their ability to wield silk, and the possession of paired fangs capable of delivering venomous bites that paralyse prey. Some spiders in warmer climates can reach extraordinary sizes. The king baboon spider *Pelinobius muticus*, has legs that could easily span a dinner plate. Others are noteworthy for their vibrant colourations. The peacock spider *Maratus volans* is one of the brightest and most elaborately decorated invertebrates on Earth.

1. PEACOCK SPIDER
The peacock spider is about 5 mm (0.2 in) long, and the male has a brightly coloured abdomen which he raises during mating dances. If the female is not impressed with his dance, she may eat him.

2. CURVED SPINY SPIDER
The long, curved spines from this spider's abdomen are thought to have evolved to deter predators, or even to mimic thorns and spines.

3. DWARF SPIDER
Members of this enormous family of spiders are called "money spiders" in the UK. Many males have different shaped growths on their abdomens, possibly used during courtship.

4. SYDNEY BROWN TRAPDOOR SPIDER
Trapdoor spiders live underground for most of their lives. They make burrows in the ground and construct trapdoors out of silk, soil, and vegetation.

5. CELLAR SPIDER
This arachnid's body is around 2–10 mm (0.08–0.4 in) long, but its legs can be up to 50 mm (2 in) long. They are found on every continent except Antarctica, where it is too cold for them to survive.

Orchard spider

6. ORCHARD SPIDER
The orchard spider has long, green legs and a particularly long abdomen covered in silver, yellow, and black markings. They can be found across the east coast of the Americas.

7. SPOTTED WOLF SPIDER
The spotted wolf spider hunts its prey on the ground, rather than weaving a web. It chases and leaps on any prey that it comes across, killing it by piercing it with its fangs.

8. AUSTRALIAN GARDEN ORB WEAVER
These orb weavers are famous for the large and intricate webs they spin at night. They are able to change their colours each time they moult to match their environment.

9. WASP SPIDER
Despite not being very venomous, the wasp spider's distinctive black-and-yellow stripes serve as a clever defence tactic, warning predators that it is dangerous and to stay away.

10. BABOON SPIDER
The baboon spider is Africa's only tarantula. They are able to make a strange and alarming noise by rubbing their legs together like a grasshopper.

11. CRAB SPIDER
A master of disguise, this spider can change colour to blend into its surroundings. It camouflages itself in flowers and patiently waits for its prey to walk by... and then pounces!

12. SPINY ORB-WEAVER
The spiny orb-weaver spider is easy to recognise by its colourful markings, crab-like shape, and large spines that protrude from its abdomen.

Spiny orb weaver

Green lynx spider

13. GREEN LYNX SPIDER

The green lynx spider has cat-like reflexes. Instead of spinning a web, it uses its camoflauge to blend into its surroundings, then ambushes insects by leaping into the air and pouncing on them like a cat.

14. MEXICAN REDKNEE TARANTULA

This spider has super-sensitive legs, and can use them to taste, smell, and even feel vibrations from the sound of approaching predators and prey.

15. BLACK HOUSE SPIDER

Black house spiders spin a messy looking web with a funnel-shaped den in the middle. The female will almost never leave the web, unless she is forced to due to danger or lack of food.

16. EUROPEAN CAVE SPIDER

The European cave spider doesn't like light, and lives in dark places like caves and tunnels. Baby cave spiders, however, are attracted to light, meaning they can scuttle to new homes.

17. BLACK WIDOW SPIDER

Considered the most venomous spider in North America, the black widow's venom is 15 times more potent than rattlesnake venom, drop for drop. Luckily, its bite is painful but rarely deadly.

18. NORTHERN SPITTING SPIDER

True to its strange name, the northern spitting spider spits a sticky, venomous substance at its prey to trap and kill it.

19. WATER SPIDER

The water spider spends its entire life underwater. It spins webs below the surface which it fills with air it carries down from the surface via little hairs on its bottom, creating its own aquatic safe-space underwater.

20. ARIAMNES COLUBRINUS

The whip spider has a long, thin body that looks a bit like a twig. They drop a couple of threads of silk below them, and when a small spider hits the threads they descend and attack.

21. GOLDEN SILK ORB WEAVER

Also known as the "banana spider", the golden silk orb weaver is one of the oldest spider species in the world, with specimens discovered from over 165 million years ago!

22. RED WIDOW SPIDER

This spider is very rare, and can only be found in certain parts of Florida. Red widows are very venomous, but very rarely come into contact with humans.

23. TRIANGULAR SPIDER

This oddly-shaped spider often dangles upon silken lines hung from leaves and branches. It waits for the vibrations of a fly buzzing past, and then grabs it using its long, strong front legs.

24. ARROW-SHAPED MICRATHENA

The name "micrathena" comes from "micro", meaning "little", and the name of the goddess Athena, who was a weaver. This brightly-coloured spider weaves webs and lies in wait for its prey.

25. YELLOW GARDEN SPIDER

This spider is known for spinning beautiful webs that are incredibly strong and can hold several heavy insects at once. Garden spiders also eat their old webs to re-use the silk!

Daring jumping spider

26. DARING JUMPER SPIDER

Phidippus audax does not spin a web, but uses its long legs to leap up to 50 times its own body length and pounce on its prey.

27. HAWAIIAN HAPPY-FACED SPIDER

This cheerful-looking spider is hard to miss! Its distinctive red-and-yellow markings make it look like it has a happy, smiling face on its back.

28. RAFT SPIDER

Raft spiders use short, waterproof hairs on their legs to walk on water. They identify prey from ripples in the water, then skate across the water's surface to attack.

29. WOODLOUSE SPIDER

While most spiders are left to fend for themselves as soon as they are born, the woodlouse spider is believed to be one of the few that looks after its young for some time when they hatch.

30. LADYBIRD SPIDER

In Britain, the ladybird spider is a threatened species, its wild habitats lost to farming. In fact, it was thought to be extinct for years, but was rediscovered in 1980.

SPIDER WEBS

Araneae silk and its uses

The order Araneae is incredibly ancient, made up of almost 50,000 known species, with many more left to discover. Spiders are likely to have walked upon the Earth long before dinosaurs and today they exist on every continent, except Antarctica.

All spiders can produce silk. Spider silk is incredibly strong and is used for climbing, building egg sacs, wrapping their prey, and famously, for spinning webs. They can even use it to travel, releasing threads and letting the wind catch them and carry them away.

They produce silk from "spinnerets", which are silk glands on their abdomens. Spiders are able to make up to seven different types of silk, producing different types depending on what they need it for. The silk is made from different proteins and is stored inside the spiders in liquid form. Spiders can also make the silk they produce sticky, secreting droplets of an adhesive onto the strands of the web that they want to use to catch prey in a different way.

Spiderwebs can take many forms, from the classic orb-web to funnel webs, spiral webs, and messy shelf webs in the corners of dusty rooms. They vary greatly in size, with the largest being the web of the Darwin's bark spider *Caerostris darwini*, which has been found spanning 25 m (82 ft).

Not all spiders weave webs – some spiders actively hunt, some hide and wait for prey to come to them, and some spiders use their silk to catch prey. A bolas spider spins a droplet (a "capture blob") of silk on the end of a line, then swings it at moths and flies. A direct hit with the sticky blob traps the prey, and the spider pulls up the line to eat its catch.

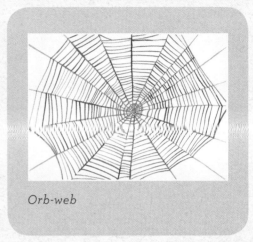

Orb-web

Australian garden orb weaver *spider*

FIGURE 2. SPIDER VENOM

Necrotic and neurotoxic attacks

All spiders have fangs. They are perfectly adapted for piercing their prey and delivering their venom.

The fangs are curved (which helps them hold the prey in place) and are hollow inside, with a small hole at the tip. This hollow duct leads through to the venom gland, and when the fang pierces the prey, it is squeezed out.

Some spiders have necrotic venom (which kills the cells and tissues around the bite) and some have neurotoxic venom (which acts directly on the nervous system, interfering with the signals to the nerves and sometimes causing breathing problems and heart failure). The strength of a spider's venom can vary, with some being much more deadly to humans than others, though all spider venom is effective on their prey, for whom it is primarily intended.

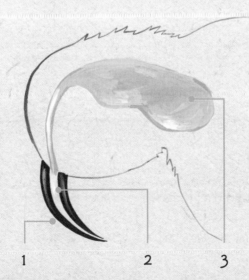

1   2   3

1. *Fang*
2. *Poison Duct*
3. *Poison Gland*

The **black widow spider** *has neurotoxic venom.*

GLOSSARY

ABDOMEN
The part of an insect's body below the thorax (not including legs).

ADAPTATION
The way an organism changes to be better at surviving and thriving in its environment.

ANISODACTYL
Having three toes facing forward and one facing backwards.

ARBOREAL
An animal who is adapted to living and moving about in trees.

AUTOTOMY
When an animal casts off part of its body while under threat (like the tail of a lizard).

BALEEN
The filter-feeding system inside the mouths of baleen whales.

BILL
Another name for a bird's beak.

CACHE
A hiding place, especially one in a tree or in the ground, for food.

CAMOUFLAGE
The way an animal may disguise itself against its environment as a defence against predators.

CARAPACE
A shield or shell (sometimes made of bone, and some of chitin) covering some or all of an animal's back.

CARNIVORE
An animal that eats only meat.

CARRION
The rotting flesh of dead animals.

CARTILAGINOUS
An animal with a skeleton that was made either partly or entirely out of cartilage.

CHRYSALIS
The casing in which a butterfly or moth encases themselves during metamorphosis.

DISPLAY
The way that an animal behaves to convey information to other animals, sometimes in the same species, sometimes in a different one.

DIASTEMA
The space between two teeth.

DIVERSITY
How different living things in a specific ecosystem are.

DORMANT
The period in an animal's life cycle where growth, development, and physical activity are temporarily stopped, for example during hibernation.

ECHOLOCATION
The biosonar system used by toothed whales, bats, and some other animals to locate objects and prey in the world around them.

ELYTRA
The pair of hardened, protective forewings on some insects, like beetles.

EMBRYO
An animal in the first stages of its development, usually still within the egg or uterus.

ENDANGERED SPECIES
A species of animals at risk of extinction for whatever reason.

EVOLUTION
The gradual changes in a specific species caused by different circumstances, including natural selection.

EXOSKELETON
The protective structure covering the outside of the body of some animals, including spiders and insects.

EXTINCT
A species that has died out and has no living members.

FLOURISH
When a living organism grows and develops in a healthy way, especially as a result of the environment it lives in.

FOLIVOROUS
An animal that eats only leaves.

FOSSORIAL
Animals who are specially adapted for digging, like moles.

HERBIVORE
An animal that eats only plants.

INVERTEBRATE
Creatures that do not have a backbone.

IRIDESCENT
A display of a rainbow spectrum of colours that shimmer and change depending on how the light hits them.

MANDIBLE
Both the lower jaw in mammals, and the pair of mouthparts used for biting and crushing food in insects.

MASSETER
The muscle that opens and closes the lower jaw.

MATING
When two animals come together to breed.

METAMORPHOSIS
A change from one form to another in the life of an animal, like the change from caterpillar to butterfly.

MIGRATION
The annual movement of animals (like butterflies or birds) from one place to another, usually to spend the winter somewhere warmer, and for breeding.

MORPHS
A specific form of one species, like a worker ant or a soldier ant.

OFFSPRING
The children, or young, of a specific species.

ORGANISM
A living thing, a specific animal, plant, fungus, or bacteria, etc.

OSTEODERMS
Bony deposits that form scales or plates in the skin of reptiles and amphibians.

OVIPOSITOR
The organ at the end of the abdomen of a female insect, used for depositing eggs.

PARASITE
An organism that lives in or on another organism in another species, living off the nutrients in its body. The other species is known as the host.

PLASTRON
The bottom of the body of a turtle, the underneath of its shell.

PLUMAGE
The feathers of a bird.

PREHENSILE
A body part that has been adapted to grasp, hold, or wrap around something, like the tail of a monkey.

PROBOSCIS
A long, flexible snout, like the trunk of an elephant, or the long, protruding mouthparts of an insect, used for sucking (like that of a butterfly).

SCLEROTIC RINGS
Sclerotic rings are rings of bone found in the eyes of several groups of vertebrates (except mammals and some reptiles). They support the eyes, especially for animals whose eyes are not spherical.

SECRETE
To create and release a substance.

SEXUAL DIMORPHISM
The difference in appearance between the male and the female of the same species.

TAXONOMY
The branch of science that classifies living things.

THORAX
The part of an insect's body between its head and abdomen (not including the legs or wings).

VEGETATION
Plant life in a specific area or region.

VENOM
The poisonous fluid that certain animals (like snakes and spiders) secrete and insert into the bodies of their prey or predators by biting or stinging.

VERTEBRATE
Creatures with a backbone.

WATTLE
The fleshy appendage that hangs down below the throat of a bird like a chicken or turkey.

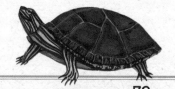

CREDITS

ILLUSTRATED BY KELSEY OSEID

WRITTEN BY JULES HOWARD AND FAY EVANS

Senior Designer: Emma Vince

Senior Editor: Fay Evans

Publisher: Donna Gregory

Weldon Owen would like to thank Jules Howard, Kelsey Oseid, Susie Rae and Hazel Eriksson for their hard work and help on this book.

Kelsey Oseid is an illustrator, author, and amateur naturalist. Her gouache illustrations focus on natural history subjects like taxonomy, biodiversity, and taxidermy, as well as related subjects like astronomy and the ways humans relate to the natural world.

Jules Howard is a zoologist, non-fiction author, and international ambassador for science. As well as writing regularly for *The Guardian* and the BBC, Jules offers support to a number of non-fiction book publishers working on zoological themes, including Weldon Owen and Bloomsbury.

Golden-crowned kinglet, Australian golden whistler, White-eyed slaty flycatcher, Hermit-thrush, Black-capped chickadee.